Claret and
Cross-Buttock
or
Rafferty's Prize-Fighters

also by Joe Robinson
The Life and Times of Francie Nichol of South Shields

Claret and Cross-Buttock

or

Rafferty's Prize-Fighters

Joe Robinson

London   George Allen & Unwin Limited
Ruskin House   Museum Street

Printed in Great Britain
in 11/12-point Baskerville type
by Willmer Brothers Limited, Birkenhead

*I dedicate this book primarily to my forbears,
but also to all those who like a good fair fight*

Author's Acknowledgements

I wish to extend my grateful thanks to the following people who have given me much help, in various ways, in writing this book: Bob Robinson, Harry Robinson and Peter Robinson (sons of Geordie and Lizzie); Harry Robinson (son of the blacksmith); Jack Robinson (son of Johnny and Francie); Mary and Walter Callaghan (sister and brother-in-law to Johnny); Nora Jones and Harold Alderman (boxing historians); Fred Charlton (boxing reporter); Lawrence Tagg and Doris Johnson (librarians); Judy Robinson (secretary).

Contents

Illustrations

Claret

'With first rate science dealt the unerring blow
Which from the sneezer made the claret flow'

(c. d. h. miles, *Pugilistica*, 3 vols, 1880–1906)

'His hits were rum, none could deny,
His blackstrap none could bear it,
But of his hogshead he was shy,
Lest they should tap his claret'

(l. fitz-barnard, *Fighting Sports*, 1921)

Cross-Buttock

'a particular lock or fall in the Broughtonian art, which conveys
more pleasurable sensations to the spectators than the patient'

(francis grose, *A Classical Dictionary of the Vulgar Tongue*, 1785)

'get his crutch upon your hip or buttock, give him a cant over
your shoulder – if well done his heels will go up in the air,
he goes over with tremendous violence, and you fall upon his
abdomen. The chances are that he is either insensible or is so
shaken by the fall that he loses all power of resisting your future
attacks'

(vincent dowling, *Fistiana, or, The Oracle of the Ring*, 1841)

Prologue

'Peter Rafferty, this court finds you guilty of the wilful murder of Brian Patrick Daly, in that at five o'clock on the morning of the seventeenth of March, eighteen-hundred and forty-six, you did meet the deceased at a place called Limerick, with the sole intention of taking his life, and that you did then and there mercilessly beat him to death with your bare hands.

'We abominate this disgusting so-called sport of pugilism and all those who support it. To see two grown men knock each other senseless for a sum of money, is one of the most degrading spectacles that could ever be imagined. However, because of the misplaced patronage of certain of the nobility, this prize-fighting is not only countenanced but is actively encouraged in certain areas of this kingdom. In your case, this encounter with your victim was not even arranged for the purposes of sport or for financial benefit, but was, by your own admission and the testimony of several witnesses, to fight to the death. And this was freely engaged upon by both parties. Because of your vanity and because previous contests with the deceased had not been resolved to your mutual satisfaction, you both decided to determine the issue by a fight which would only terminate on the death of one or other of the participants. For more than four hours you battered each other until Daly fell dead. There are no extenuating circumstances and I have no alternative but to sentence you to be taken away and, at the proper time and place, hanged by the neck until you are dead. The court will note that the application of Messrs Fowchester and Chalmers for the earthly remains is granted. The prisoner's body will be delivered into their hands for dissection after it has hung for the customary period. May Almighty God have mercy on your soul.'

1

Rafferty

My name is John Robinson and Peter Rafferty was my grandfather. And that is one speech which even I know by heart.

At the time all this happened – which was almost fifty years before I was born – Peter Rafferty was a famous bare-knuckle fighter in Ireland. Those times weren't easy, especially in Ireland. Potatoes were all that most of the Irish lived on and when they got the Rot thousands of people starved to death. The English newspapers used to talk about the Irish as though they had no spunk. They used to say that the Irish peasants would just lay down and die. But they took a long time in the dyin'. It's a wonder there were any of them left at all, that many had been carted off to the colonies. All they wanted was enough space to grow a few spuds. But even that was denied to them. A spud will grow almost anywhere and if ye could find a little wild plot somewhere that hadn't been fenced in, then maybe ye could stay alive. But that became next to impossible. Hundreds upon hundreds used to roam the country lookin' for scraps and if they found a few spuds growin' in a field and nobody about, who could blame them for takin' a couple – even if they did belong to someone else. And Jesus knows what would happen to them if they were caught – even with only one tatty old rotten spud in their hand when ye could be hanged for takin' the slop out of a pig's mouth.

Peter Rafferty was one of the lucky ones. He could make a livin' by his fists. At that time, when a fighter was well known, matches would be arranged for him by somebody with a lot of money – usually one of the gentry or a rich merchant. In the main, though, it would be a lord or squire who would put up the money because it came so easy to them that they didn't care about gamblin' a few thousand pounds whereas the businessman who had to work for his, was a mite more careful. The fightin' men might be paid £5 each, sometimes winner takin' all, but more often than not it was a lot less. Most of the money they made was either by bettin' on themselves or on somebody else. If the backers had huge sums at stake, they would usually see to it that their man was well fed and in good physical condition. In this case they would hire a trainer who would be with the fighter night and day for several weeks before the mill — as they called it — took place. The two of them would stay at an inn specially prepared for the job and get only the best of food. It was the trainer's job not only to see that his man was physically fit but also to make sure that he wasn't knobbled by any of the other party's camp before comin' up to scratch.

So a man like my grandfather, if he was strong and tough and got plenty of good fights, could count himself blessed. Peter Rafferty could look after himself in any company, was better fed than most of his countrymen, and respected by those whose opinion he cared about.

This particular English judge had been after Rafferty for a long time and when he finally got his hands on him, he dealt with Rafferty with as much mercy as Rafferty had shown Daly. His defiance and frank speakin' was probably his undoin' as much as anythin'. He had given no quarter and had asked for none in return. He was a giant and a dangerous one at that. And the English in Ireland wanted to be rid of the likes of him.

Well, they took him away and put him in gaol until it suited them to hang him. The gaols in Ireland were a lot worse than most of the English ones, because even in Newgate ye could live in comfort if ye had the money or the right connections. Ye could buy liquor, good food, fancy clothes and whores, have servants, and even carry on your life's business all without ever steppin' outside the walls of the prison. What the gaoler wasn't allowed to supply ye with ye could still get if ye bribed him enough. In fact, ye could do almost anythin' inside that ye could do outside, provided ye had the necessary

But if ye hadn't, then life in Newgate was as hellish as it was anywhere else.

Such goin's on didn't usually happen in the Irish gaols because most of the prisoners were wretched poor. So ye got a different type of gaoler altogether. There, it was a hated occupation – not like that of the English ones where there was keen rivalry for a position which was esteemed because of the power and chances for money-makin' that it fetched. Nearly all the prisoners in Irish gaols were Irish. Ye didn't get the Jews that ye got in England for a start, and most of the foreigners were either English or Scotch colonists brought across to own the land and tame the Irish. Not all the English were bad but if they showed any favours to the Irish they were sharp punished for it – usually by bein' stripped of their property and possessions and brought back to England in disgrace. Some of them were gaoled or transported for what were serious crimes like speakin' Irish or marryin' an Irish girl – and who could blame them for that. There is no such thing as an unlovely Irish lass although there was plenty of ugliness amongst the pampered English with all their corsets and things and their rich sickly foods. They never moved off their fat backsides unless it was to get into a horse and carriage. Show me a really bonny English girl now and I'll show ye a hard worker who's not frightened of a bit of wind and rain.

At the time that Peter Rafferty was in gaol there were people there for all kinds of things. A poacher who'd been caught with a wild rabbit, a feller who had stolen a dog. A kid who had pinched a tanner, and a widow-with-nine-bairns who'd found a half-crown and kept it. Labourers who'd tried to form a union, a soldier who stole a pocket-handkerchief. And even a feller who had spoken rudely to a Member of Parliament in the street. An old man who had taken a short cut across a field and was had up for trespassin'. And even a rat-catcher. Apparently this rat-catcher used to get paid £1 per year for riddin' a farmer of all his rats. After three years of this work the farmer decided not to pay him for the last year because he thought there were no rats left to catch so he wouldn't be needin' this feller any more. The rat-catcher had pleaded with the farmer all he could, tellin' him that

he had the bailiff to pay, but the farmer would have none of
it. A few weeks later, the rat-catcher had come back with a
big sack on his back and asked the farmer for the money
that was owin'. Just once more. No sooner had the farmer
refused than the rat-catcher up-ended the sack and emptied
out fifty-two live rats inside the farmer's house. And that's
why the rat-catcher ended up where he was now. There were
very few adulterers and rapers about. Murderers, yes – plenty
of them. But the others were sins against God, not just against
man, and they weren't natural crimes.

It wasn't enough that ye did no harm to anybody or their
property, ye couldn't even speak your mind. If ye took an oath,
even in private, and the wrong people heard about it, ye could
be put away – one way or another. They said it was because
of the blasphemy. But it wasn't. It was the reason for takin'
the oath that got ye into trouble – like joinin' a union to protect your wife and kids. One bloke who had got himself drunk
and peed up against the wheel of a carriage when some important Lady had been inside, was given two years' hard
labour. After the judge had read out the sentence, this feller
boldly asks him what wage he would be gettin' for his labour,
and the judge was so vexed that he sentenced him to transportation for five years.

Of course there were no lawyers to state the case of the
poor man and often as not if ye were up for poachin', or
settin' fire to a haystack, the magistrate or whatever would
turn out to be the owner of the land or the haystack so ye
couldn't expect a fair trial with the likes of that. Keepin'
people in prison cost the tax-payers money and because it was
useless to fine people who couldn't pay, the choice was usually
between transportation or the gallows. It depended on the
whim of the particular judge which one ye got. If it was
transportation and ye survived the journey out, the chances
of your ever returnin' to your homeland were about the same
as a snowball's in Hell. If ye got the gallows, then the losin'
of your life was only the half of it. From the time ye were
sentenced to the time they pressed the lever they were always
on to ye night and day to make confessions. And when ye
were taken away to the Tree, ye had to face all the people

who had come to see ye strung up. Sometimes there'd be hundreds, and sometimes thousands. Ye were taken on a hurdle which was dragged right through the town by a big dirty horse with ye facin' its tail. Your arms were chained behind your back, the noose of the rope was already round your neck, and the sheriff sat opposite ye with a loaded blunderbuss. Dependin' on what the crowd believed about ye, ye might attract stones and jeers or screams and tears. When ye got to the place ye had to climb the scaffold and then make a speech to the crowd tellin' them what a bad man ye were and how ye were not fit to live. How the sentence was just and how ye deserved to die.

Then ye had to tell them not to be like yourself or they would get the same as you were goin' to get. On top of all that, ye were expected to actually tip the executioner – the bloke that was goin' to turn ye off, and do ye in. After it was all over and ye had hung for an hour, they either sent ye to some doctors to be cut up and have your innards played about with, or ye were hung in chains in some public place so that even your rottin' carcase would be scorned by all who passed by. And the punishment to any of your friends or relatives for pullin' ye down to give you a decent burial, was seven years' transportation. So even though the judge's last words had been that he hoped God would have mercy on your soul, ye had to keep Him waitin' until, by hook or by crook, ye could get laid in your grave.

It was a good job for Rafferty that they never seemed to be in too much of a hurry to get the hangin' done in those days. They probably thought that givin' the prisoners plenty of time to think would be good for their souls. Because while he was waitin' in Dublin Gaol, some of the sportin' squires had got up a petition to try and save his life. Probably more because he was a good income rather than because he was bein' too harshly punished for a crime which, after all is said and done, was a fair fight. Granted the stakes were a bit higher but if Rafferty had lost then Daly would have gone to the gallows instead.

Anyway, the outcome of the petition was that Peter Rafferty's death sentence was changed to transportation, so that instead of bein' hanged in Ireland he was to spend the rest of his life slavin' for the English in an Australian penal colony.

2

Convict's Reprieve

My grandfather was taken in chains from Dublin Gaol to the shore and he and the rest of a gang of twelve prisoners had to row two miles out to the prison ship. This was called a convict hulk, and as it had once been a convict transporter which was no longer seaworthy, it was fitted out with dungeons, chains, floggin' triangles. The lot. All the necessary to prepare the prisoners – who were now called convicts – for a voyage that would kill a good many of them and break the health and spirits of the rest.

The convicts were kept in these floatin' gaols for two or three months until there was a full load, and also to find out which ones were strong enough to survive such conditions. If you were still on your feet after a couple of months, the ship's surgeon passed ye fit for transportation. If ye weren't, you were sent back to the gaol on land to give ye a chance to regain your strength before bein' tried out on board again. And if ye were dead, ye were just heaved over the side without fuss or favour.

The hulks were far worse than any land gaols. The ship's surgeon only came aboard for a weekly inspection, so there was no medical aid at all. The only skill he needed was to be able to pick the dead from the dyin'. And those in a bad way with a disease that was likely to affect the other convicts wouldn't get the benefit of the doubt. Not that any of the doctors of those days had much idea anyway. Blood lettin', horseridin' and miracle waters were the only cures they knew and these were only for the rich. They weren't interested in people who were scruffy and couldn't pay their high charges.

There were three dungeon decks on the hulks. The worse the convict – the lower the deck and the heavier the chain. Peter Rafferty was put in the bottom deck. There was about thirty convicts on each deck with one open privvy in the middle. The grub was foul. There wasn't enough of it but nobody wanted any more. There were so many fleas, lice, mice and rats that ye just had to get used to them. Ye couldn't drive them away and they knew it. If ye scratched, ye drew blood. And then ye got more. Some were too weak to scratch. They just gave up. What could ye do, chained to a man lousy with vermin? Rats at women's breasts, flies in their behinds. Fleas on their body, corruption in their livers, and poison in their guts. The stench of sour piss, vomit and human shit was always there even when the decks had been scrubbed – and they were sluiced twice a day. The bilge always leaked through to the bottom deck where it collected into stinkin' pools.

The commonest cause of death by far was gaol-fever. Headaches, chills, pains in the belly and then death after three weeks. If ye went mad ye were chained by your neck to a beam so that if ye moved or slithered down, ye throttled yourself.

The daily routine was strict and there was no excuse for not bein' able to read:

5.30 a.m.	Rise and get washed
6.00 a.m.	Clean ship
7.30 a.m.	Stone-breaking on shore
12 noon	Dinner meal
12.45 p.m.	Stone-breaking, or other shore labour
4.30 p.m.	Muster of prisoners
4.45 p.m.	Supper meal
5.15 p.m.	General cleaning duties
7.30 p.m.	Ablutions and prayers
8.00 p.m.	Into hammocks or bunks
8.15 p.m.	Hatches battened down

Every day somebody jumped overboard and was either weighed down and drowned by his own chains, or shot if he came up. A few made it. But very few. And none from Peter Rafferty's ship. Every now and again a whore got on board and made as much mischief as the worst of the vermin.

After two months, the *Hoogley* – I think it was – which was an old sailin' ship of about 450 ton, came from Gravesend to Cork. It had been chartered to take convicts to Sydney in Australia. The captain boarded the brig where Peter Rafferty was, and told the surgeon to sort out 200 of the fittest convicts. But that he wouldn't take them on board his ship until the troops arrived. This captain used to organise press-gangs which got men drunk – seamen or not – and then cart them off to the man-o'-war ships of the Royal Navy. Most of the men who fought and died in sea battles with the French and other enemy ships were fellers who had been taken on board against their will and then forced to fight for their own lives as well as England's might. Everybody hated the impressment officers – wives and children of the men captured, and even volunteer seamen and ships' officers who knew they were gettin' crews of unskilled and resentful men who would escape at the first chance they got. These men would jump ship at foreign ports hopin' to work their passage back on a merchant-man and risk being executed as deserters. The wages were poor and the conditions and food so terrible that there was little to attract a man to join the navy. Consequently the sailor of the early part of the 1800s was usually of the worst kind that ever served under the British flag. This captain, and all those like him, wouldn't venture to take a shipload of convicts and mutinous sailors across the seas without the backin' of musket soldiers. And no decent ship's officer would volunteer for the convict ships.

When the troops arrived, Peter Rafferty and the rest were herded in chains on board the *Hoogley*. All the time the soldiers kept firin' their muskets over the heads of the prisoners. The idea was to break the spirits of the wildest of them so that by the time they landed in Australia they would be as tame as rabbits through discipline and starvation. Dangerous prisoners like Rafferty carried sixteen pounds worth of chains and he was manacled from a band around his neck to an eleven-pound basil around his ankle. The basil was linked up to the basils on up to twenty other prisoners so that if one of them moved they were all jerked. Rafferty was again put on the lowest deck which was always flooded with the stinkin' bilge water. Every afternoon he was brought on deck for an hour's exercise to shuffle round and round the deck draggin' the rest behind him. The only other times he got up on deck was when he and the others were forced at gun-point to watch the floggin's. Five hundred lashes with the cat was common. This was a whip with nine leather thongs each tipped with lead barbs to rip the flesh apart.

After a while, seein' men flogged – sometimes to death and then chucked overboard – became so ordinary that everybody got used to it. The same fellers would be flogged day in day out, and because the wounds never got a chance to heal, their backs would still be red raw before the next floggin' even started. The bosun and the other hard lads would take turns each, passin' the whip over when the captain decided they were too tired to do much more good.

One very hot afternoon, this skinny feller who was tied to the triangle was bein' thrashed.

'Open the bastard's belly so's I can see his guts!' shouted the First Mate.

The skinny feller had been thrashed every day for the past three weeks and as a result he had lost the use of both his legs. His hands were like suet puddin's. The flesh hung off his back and the tops of his legs, and when they douched him with brine after each hidin', ye could see the white of his bones. Yet day after day the silly bugger would do somethin' daft so they had an excuse to do him again. Always they carried him away unconscious. Today he had thrown his food on the floor because there was a rat's tail floatin' in it. Anybody else would have just chucked away the tail and ate the rest. But not him.

'Give's it here, ye whore's spawn!' yelled the Mate. He took the whip and lashed it round the skinny feller's neck and the skinny feller vomited blood and sick which dribbled down his face and chest and down his legs.

'So, you're broke, are ye? Ye gutless spineless bastard! By the time I'm finished with ye, ye'll be screamin' like all the devils in Hell.' He raised the whip over his shoulder and bent to the waist.

'Enough!!'

Big Rafferty was now standin' square between the Mate and the skinny feller. His quick movement had dragged some of the fellers he was chained to to the ground.

'Why, ye fuckin' Irish bastard, I'll whip the livin' daylights out of ye!'

Rafferty, who was a very softly spoken sort of man, says to him quietly so's only he could hear, 'If you take that bunch of hairs to me then ye'd better see that I'm flogged to death before ye cut me down. 'Cos if ye don't, I'll rive your arms out of their sockets.'

This ugly sod of a Mate just turned and walked away. Rafferty nodded his head to one of the soldiers who were standin' there on guard and he cut the skinny feller down. The captain and the surgeon, who were always present at the floggin's, just looked at each other but didn't interfere. And nobody said not a word.

Rafferty went down below decks and the other prisoners followed.

'Ye shouldn't have done that, Paddy. He's a mean one that. He'll get ye before this trip's done. And that's for sure.'

'Leave me to worry about that, ye silly bastard. I'm not sure that ye don't deserve all ye get.'

From then on, the skinny feller was always hangin' around Peter Rafferty. Always tryin' to get out of him what he'd done to get transported. But Rafferty kept his mouth shut.

'Everybody talks about Botany Bay, but we ain't goin' there. Nobody goes there any more. There's more cons there than settlers now and the settlers are terrified. I'll bet ye anythin' we'll all end up in Tasmania. Not that it matters. It's hell anywhere in that God-forsaken place. I should know, I spent fourteen years there.'

'What are ye goin' back for then, skinny feller?' asked Rafferty.

'They didn't give me no choice. I would've picked America.

It's good there. Warm it is. But cool enough. Not like the hellfire we're goin' to. It's only a short voyage and they looks after ye 'cos they put ye up for auction, and the more ye fetch, the more the captain gets. The captain used to get six guineas for your body when I was first sent to Botany, and the surgeon got ten bob if ye got there in one piece. So ye can guess who got served. Me mother and father got transported in 1799 for robbery. Three of me brothers went with them. Me sister died on the hulk before we even got started. I was born on the way out. Me mother died the day after. Even though she was big with me, they shaved her and caned her every day for five days durin' the week before I was born. One of the seamen had dragged her down on the deck and tried to have his way with her and she had spat in his face. When the bosun had come up, she did the same to him. Me brother had grabbed the bosun's arm while he was kickin' me mother in the belly. They put him in the sweat-box. Mind there was some hard women. They used to let them fight it out amongst themselves. Scratchin' and kickin' and cursin'. Most of them were whores of the cons, the crew and the soldiers. That was the only way they could get enough food to eat or a bit of fresh air. On the deck we were on – which was only the middle one – the air was so bad durin' the night, that the candle used to go out. Wait till we get to the tropics. Ye can be lyin' there watchin' the melted pitch drippin' down on ye and ye cannot even move out of its way.

'We are supposed to get as much rations as the soldiers and the crew. But they keep stuff back and sell it. I've seen fresh water fetch two bob a pint. It took us six months to get there. Me three brothers died of gaol-fever, so only me and me father made it.

'He got put with a swine of a planter and escaped into the bush. The natives caught him and cut his ears off and burnt his members to a cinder. Ye can't blame the poor buggers in a way. It was the settlers that started it by killin' every black they laid eyes on. So any white man has had it if they come across him. Me father gave himself up in the finish and they sent him to Norfolk Island as a punishment. Ye got flogged more often there than ye did in Botany, even. Ye'd spend

ten hours a day bakin' in the sun smashin' rocks, all chained
up. The flies would never keep off ye. And after a while ye
gave up. Ye just let them eat your sores.

'There was no penalty less than seventy-five strokes. Every
day, fellers would just go stark ravin' mad and stay that way.
They had a sweat-box there as well but it was a lot worse
than this one. The law says they can't put ye in for more
than six hours at a time, but over there it's different. They'll
keep ye in there for six days. Out in that hellish sun they have
there. The box is so small that ye have to kneel with your
head crouched down. Once a day they open the latch and
stick a bowl of dirty water with a bit of bread floatin' in it
and ye have to lap it up like a dog because your arms are
chained behind your back. When ye come out, you're blind
for as many days as you've been cooped up. Me father was
always in trouble and always sick with the colic. One day,
he and this other con did what many others before them had
done. They tossed up to see who would do it. The other feller
won. He just turned his back and straight away me father
smashed his skull open with the stone mallet. They took me
father away to Sydney and hanged him. I was twelve then.
Two years later I escaped and worked me passage back. I
turned to me father's old trade and eventually it caught up
with me. And here I am.'

One afternoon Rafferty was up on deck for his constitu-
tional when the captain's daughter – a little girl of about
eight – fell overboard into a rough sea. Although Rafferty's
legs were still chained, he and the rest of his gang had long
since so worked on their chains that they could slip the links
when they went below decks. This way they could make
themselves more comfortable. At least if they turned over in
the night or wanted to be sick they wouldn't have to drag
everybody else with them.

Rafferty unhooked himself and dived straight over the side,
chains and all. Even though his rations weren't anywhere near
enough for a man of his size, he was still immensely strong.
He grabbed the little girl by the hair and swam behind the
ship till they got a rope to him. With the girl under one arm
he hauled himself up with the other.

The captain had him in his cabin and told him that he would have to be put back in chains until they got to Australia. But if he promised to keep his mouth shut he would take him back to England on the return trip. He told my grandfather he would have to change his name and never go back to Ireland. And that if he was ever caught then the captain would say that he had escaped. And to remember that the punishment for returnin' from transportation, was death.

3

Gypsies

A year later, after workin' as a matelot and visitin' many ports collectin' cargo for the return journey, the ship docked at Gravesend and Peter Robinson – as Rafferty now called himself – made his way to Gloucester. Bristol was the next most important prize-fightin' place to London, and it seemed the most natural place to head for.

No sooner there, than my grandfather was engaged in fightin' again. He soon made a name for himself and was invited to London for a match. The fight had only just begun when the Runners – London Peelers – who were planted in the crowd, jumped the ropes to grab Peter Robinson. Both he and the bloke he was fightin' got stuck into the Runners. The seconds and ring-men joined in and there was a right royal battle.

'Quick, Peter, beat it! Take this horse and get out of it as fast as you can.'

My grandfather jumped clean over the ropes and into the crowd who made way for him. On to the horse and away he went like a bat out of hell. The whole crowd let them by. And Peter Robinson got clean away.

He galloped southwest and into Hampshire ridin' solid through the night. By the next mornin' he was starvin' hungry. Big as he was Rafferty could run a wild rabbit into the ground any day of the week. And when he saw a couple of them in this field he jumped the horse over the hedge. It landed in a ditch, broke its leg and rolled over. Rafferty forgot about the rabbit.

'Holy Jesus,' he says to himself.

'Ye poor bastard,' he says to the horse. He stroked its leg and sat down beside it.

'Ye've served me well,' he says, 'and I've never had a chance to have a good look at ye before now. But you're a beautiful lookin' beast. I'll tell ye that. By Jesus, ye are.'

The horse lay writhin' on the ground and wouldn't eat the handful of grass Rafferty stuck in its mouth.

'It's just what ye need,' he says. 'It'll do ye the world of good. It's long and it's green and it's juicy, just what you've been wantin'. Aye, but it's broken all right,' he says, with his hand on the big lump stickin' out of the horse's right-hand back leg. 'I see you're a stallion as well, eh? Wait here, I'll be gone and back in no time at all.'

Rafferty snapped a branch of a tree, tore his shirt into shreds and tied up the horse's leg. He tried to get it to its feet by shovin' and pressin' his shoulder under its back, but whenever the horse stumbled to its feet it fell down again with a loud crack.

'Well now, I'm beat but I don't know what to do with ye,' says Rafferty.

'I think I'll have to just leave ye here to get better yourself.' He started tearin' up lumps of grass by the roots and puttin' it near the horse's head so's it'd have enough to live on till it got well again.

'That's no use at all,' says a voice. 'It'll die if you leave it like that.' Rafferty turns 'round and sees here's this gypsy feller standin' lookin' at him.

'Oh, so you know what you're talkin' about, I'm to suppose,' says Rafferty.

The gypsy leaps over the hedge and the ditch and lands astride the horse. He felt the horse and the breaks in its leg.

'You're only makin' it worse, Mister,' he says, feelin' the horse all over. He unstrapped the bandage that Rafferty had put on and threw the branch away in disgust.

The anger welled up in Rafferty's throat and he would have taken the gypsy by the scruff and tossed him back across the hedge except that the horse seemed quieted for the first time since the accident. Where before it had seemed in much pain, it now seemed at ease as the gypsy was talkin' to it and strokin' it all over.

'Ye seem to have a way with him,' Rafferty says to the gypsy. 'Do ye think you can mend him?'

'Yes, I know I can. And he's a fine horse.'

'Right, he's yours,' says Rafferty. 'If you can make him well again ye can keep him. I'm away now.'

'You won't get any rabbits out of this field either, Mister. We've got every hole snared.'

'Is that right now?' says Rafferty. 'We'll soon see about that. I'll bet this good knife against your leather belt that I catch the next one ye see before it can get to any of your lousy traps.'

'Done,' says the gypsy. 'There's a big jack. Go get him if you can.'

Without fuss or favour Rafferty was up and after it in a flash. Ten minutes later he came back with a rabbit hangin' by its ears in each hand, still wrigglin'.

'Here,' he says, flingin' one across to the gypsy who drops it. 'There's one for yourself.' The gypsy's had no sooner hit the ground than it was away like a shot.

Rafferty broke the neck of his own.

'Never mind, we'll share this one.' While the gypsy tended to the horse, Rafferty stripped the rabbit and pulled its guts out.

'I'm Mungalo,' said the gypsy.

'I'm Peter,' says Rafferty. 'Peter Robinson.'

While they ate the rabbit raw, they talked. Mungalo told Rafferty that his father was the chief of a tribe and that if he wanted to, Rafferty could join them.

'They'll never find you with us,' said Mungalo. 'Nobody would give you away or we'd cut his throat.'

'What makes ye think anybody's after me?' says Rafferty. The gypsy just winked and they both laughed.

'Here's your belt, big man. I think it'll fit you now.'

So Rafferty joined up with the gypsies. He respected them and they respected him. He travelled all over with them in their wooden wagons and whenever they came anywhere near a town, Rafferty would go to Mass. Even though they didn't believe in God, they never said a word to Rafferty. After a while he picked up the Romany language. He said ye had to because the only time the gypsies speak the truth is when they're speakin' in their own tongue.

Rafferty became very attached to Mungalo who was not only kind-hearted towards children, like all gypsies, but was a wonderful fiddler. And Rafferty loved the fiddle like a pig loves shit. The dancin' and singin' that went on every night suited Rafferty right down to the ground. And he was no mean singer and dancer himself.

He got used to the smell of the gypsy and even got a taste for roasted hedgehog. But the thievin' and the beggin' he never liked. He'd rather starve to death than go cap in hand for a crust. God prefers starvers to beggars. And robbers to both. They took Rafferty for what he was and never pressed him. They went about their business, and he about his own without anybody askin' any questions. Now and then army deserters would come into the camp and no matter who or what they were, the gypsies always gave them a welcome even though they would always keep their eyes open and keep their own counsel.

Rafferty said that if ye won a gypsy's friendship with alcohol and tobacco – which they all loved, man and woman alike – that was the only way ye'd keep it.

What Rafferty particularly liked about the gypsy was his way of acceptin' his lot without whinin'. That and the way they always held themselves erect and were quick in their movements and light on their feet. But he could never get used to the way that even Mungalo could never look him straight in the eye for very long.

There were seven caravans in all, and the group that Rafferty travelled with were all either tinkers or comb-makers.

They could patch a copper sieve with only a hammer so's it would hold air, never mind water. And do anythin' with gold. To make combs, they used to cut the horns off a bull in a field in broad daylight, heat it over a fire, shape it, let it cool and then saw the teeth. Afterwards they would polish it with wood ash from the same fire. Rafferty could never get the hang of the copper smithyin' and wasn't interested in the makin' of combs. However, he certainly knew a damn sight more about horses by the time he ended up. He watched them prime an old nag with arsenic to brighten its eyes, and liven up its tail so that it looked like a racehorse. They even drilled its teeth with a cobbler's awl and filled them with birchwood so's ye couldn't tell the difference.

My grandfather hadn't been with the gypsies very long before the whole lot of them – the menfolk that is – got into one hell of a brawl in a pub one night. Amongst themselves they fought with clubs and knives, but they knew that outside they'd get hung for it. This night they were up against a bunch of sailors. And what a sow's ear they made of it. For every three sailors Rafferty looked after, it took six gypsies to hold their own. Seein' as they were outnumbered three to one, the gypsies and Rafferty took a bit of a hidin'. The next day, Rafferty took it upon himself to show the gypsies how to handle themselves. After a month or two, at the slightest provocation, the gypsies would be usin' their fists with those outside their own circle and amongst themselves.

One day Mungalo's mother began to die. The gypsies have little time for ailments and after the old woman had tried their herbs without success they gave up and said that she hadn't many days left. She went down very quick after that and so they took her outside to die and covered her with a blanket. Gypsies like to die outside and they know that if they die inside the caravan it will have to be burnt after they're gone. When Mungalo's mother went they all sobbed out loud for hours and hours. Then they buried her in a ditch and forgot about it. They then moved on somewhere else after leavin' a sign for any other gypsies who happened to be passin' that way.

A week later, Mungalo's sister ran away with another gypsy

without askin' permission to get married. When they came
back a few days afterwards, Mungalo's father slapped her
cheeks and the mother and father of the feller did the same
to him. And that was the end of the matter. When the baby
was about to be born, Mungalo's sister went outside away
from the rest and had it by herself. No help. The gypsies regard
this sort of woman and her clothes as unclean. Since there
was no cold water nearby at the time, she licked the baby
clean like a dog does its pup. She suckled that kid for three
years and durin' the second year suckled an orphan pig at the
same time.

Gypsies have a dread of prison. They hate bein' locked up.
When Mungalo's father was put in prison for stealin' a goat,
he got consumption and was dead in less than five months.

People say that gypsies steal children but Rafferty said
there was no truth in it. He remembered many young women
would bring their bastards to the gypsies knowin' they would
be well cared for.

Rafferty earned his keep by teachin' the art of self-defence
whenever they camped near a town. Lords and squires and
the likes would be his main customers. Poor people could
usually look after themselves with a stick or knife. But boxin'
was becomin' a sport for the posh and well-to-do. Rafferty
was an all-round man with more strength than skill – and of
that he had plenty. He would go into the market place or
into the middle of a horse fair and challenge any man to put
him down by fair means or foul. He couldn't risk advertisin'
himself in the newspapers in case he was recognised so had
to make do with local fights seekin' out the champion of
whatever place he found himself in. Although the villagers
would all be cheerin' on their man, Rafferty always had plenty
of support from the gypsies who would yell at the tops of
their voices whilst crackin' their whips and throwin' their hats
into the air. They used to make money by bettin' on him and
he never let them down.

Although Rafferty would never dream of insultin' the
gypsies, the way they cooked their food didn't always suit
him. He didn't mind them usin' manure for fuel, but he
never fancied eatin' stuff with flies in it – a thing which never

bothered the gypsies. Also he could never agree with them
that the meat from an animal which had died tasted better
than from one that had been killed. They could never bear
to be alone or out at night, but neither of these things ever
bothered Rafferty who would often go off on his own for
days on end lookin' for a good fight. And whenever he came
back they would all welcome him as though he had returned
from the dead. They always feared somethin' would happen
to him because of his habit of walkin' through the night. But
Rafferty loved walkin' and would never travel inside a wagon,
always preferrin' to walk out in front at the head of the train.
Neither wind nor rain bothered him. He would just carry on
till either the sun came out or the efforts of his own exertions
dried his clothes out.

One day, in the year 1851, the gypsies had a big meetin'.
Mungalo was accused of havin' been with this other gypsy's
wife. Their laws were very strict about things like that. Now
Rafferty knew that the real culprit was Mungalo's young
brother and that Mungalo was protectin' him. But because
Mungalo had made Rafferty promise to say never a word
but to keep out of the whole matter, he held his tongue. It
was gypsy business and they had their own reasons for doin'
things.

They gave Mungalo a very short trial, lastin' about fifteen
minutes, and then sentenced him to death by knifin'. In no
time at all he was ringed by five gypsies with daggers. Mungalo
kept quiet all along until Rafferty pushed his way into the
centre of the circle and told them he'd kill the first man to
lay a hand on Mungalo. Mungalo was really angry and threw
himself at Rafferty to shove him outside the circle again. 'I've
told you, Peter. You have given me your word. Do you want
them to think me a coward!'

Rafferty stood aside whilst they stabbed Mungalo again
and again, and then stepped back while the blood squirted
out of him in all directions. Mungalo still never uttered a
word apart from a bit of gurglin'. Then he went down and
that was the finish. They next took the woman and ordered
her to strip herself naked. And that is a terrible disgrace in
itself seein' as gypsy husbands are never allowed to see their

own wives in that condition. Next, they strapped her over a barrel, and, startin' with the chief, every man hit her once with a cane across her back and then spat at her. Everyone of them in turn did the same to her. She then screamed out that it wasn't Mungalo, but his brother. But the brother had vanished. Then they held her down and cut off half an ear so that from that day onwards every gypsy she met would know exactly what she had done.

Without any fuss, they broke Mungalo's little finger and tied a note of paper money to it with a red ribbon. They dropped him into a hole already dug, poured a few drops of wine on him and laid his fiddle on his chest. Then they covered him up with earth. No coffin. No cross. No sign to show that anybody was buried there.

Rafferty stood over the grave and crossed himself. Then he just walked away. What few possessions he had, he left behind him.

4

Fairground

1851, and Rafferty was just turned thirty. A few weeks after leavin' the gypsies, he was standin' on a village green with hands in his pockets watchin' a performin' troupe of travellin' showmen.

'Roll up! Roll up!' shouts this great big feller with a huge grizzly bear on the end of a chain.

'Half-a-crown to any man who will wrestle with Bonzo, here! Come on, gentlemen. Who dares take on my bear? No takers?'

'Can you wrestle it, mister?' asks Rafferty.

'Saint Patrick, not only can I fight him, I can beat him.

What's more, I could take you on at the same time and beat the both of you.'

'We'll soon see about that,' says Rafferty pushin' the crowd aside and leapin' on to the stage which was about six feet from the ground. He landed on the feet of the showman, with his hands still in his pockets. The crowd cheered and laughed like hell. Rafferty turned and grinned at them and then asked the showman if the rules allowed him to take his hands out of his pockets. The showman was in a right rage, but when he saw the size of the great muscular man who was still standin' on his toes, he says, 'I couldn't see you properly before, sir.' The crowd started booin' and shoutin' at him. So he held up his hand and said, 'I'll tell you what I'll do, folks. Come inside this tent, a penny a head, and if this fine-looking gentleman can last five minutes with this here bear, I'll give him an extra shilling for every round he can go with me.' In no time the tent was packed full.

Rafferty grabbed the bear's paws to look at its claws.

'Don't worry, mister,' whispers the showman. 'They're all filed short. You've got to do that with these buggers or they'd tear you to shreds with a single swipe.'

'That makes it fair enough by me,' says Rafferty. 'I just wanted to make sure they weren't any longer than mine so's I won't have an unfair advantage.'

He held up his hands to the crowd to show them his nails in mockery. The crowd laughed and yelled louder than ever.

'Go on, Paddy boy! Tear his pussy-cat to pieces! Chuck it through the ceiling!'

Rafferty tried to throw the bear by takin' it in a wrestlin' manner but it was far too big and heavy. However, when the bear closed on him it couldn't crush him because of his powerful arms which he extended. Neither of them was makin' much headway until Rafferty fetched it such a smash in the nose with his massive fist that blood and snot gushed out all over the place. Instead of goin' crazy, as Rafferty half-expected, the bear did off. The crowd went wild and demanded that the wrestlin' showman be brought on to get his desserts as well. All praise to the showman, because in he came, dressed in leather straps with metal studs all over.

Rafferty says to him, 'Look, mister, if ye wear that fancy suit, and I wrestle with ye, I'll get hacked to pieces.'

By this time the crowd had gone crazy and a dozen of them had climbed on to the platform.

'We'll cut them off, Paddy,' they said, pullin' out knives.

'No,' says Rafferty. 'Leave him be. If he wants to fight like that, let him. But don't expect any more courtesies from me,' he says to the showman. With that, he laid the showman out cold on the floor with a single punch between the eyes. The crowd then started pullin' the tent down and overturnin' everythin'. One of them grabbed the moneybox and made off with it.

'Fetch that back!' roared Rafferty. 'Or I'll scramble your brains! I haven't been paid yet. Bugger off, the lot of ye! You've had your money's worth. He did what he said he would, and ye can't blame him for that.'

There was no water, but there was a bottle of liquor inside an open chest. Rafferty sloshed some in the showman's face and drank the rest down himself. When the tent emptied, just Rafferty and the showman were left. He shook him.

'Sorry, mister, but ye only got what ye deserved. Give's me money and I'll be away.'

With his prize money in his pocket, Rafferty left.

A little while later, Rafferty was havin' a beer in a nearby alehouse when the bear-wrestler came in.

'I heard you were in here ... Look, sir, I owe you my thanks. My wife saw all that happened. You saved me a lot of trouble ... And money. What about joining up with me? You could travel with our show ...'

'Listen, mister, that was just a bit of fun. I fight men, not bloody bears.'

'I know, I can see that. What I meant was that a big tough fellow like yourself would be very useful. You would get all the fighting you could want if you came with us. I can promise you that. We are part of a big fair. We're going to join up with the rest of them in Nottingham at the end of the week. There's bound to be something that would suit you.'

'Wait till I've done here, then I'll let ye know. I'll come and seek ye if I decide.'

Rafferty joined the fair at Nottingham in charge of the gaff-lads. These were roughs who couldn't do any tricks or anythin' like that. Their job was to put up the tents and do all the heavy fetchin' and carryin'. They were very poorly paid and so they would pinch anythin' they could get their hands on. Pickpocketin' and tappin' – Tappin' was givin' short change. It took a man like Rafferty to keep a firm hold on these lads.

This fair had all the usual attractions. Monsters, salamanders, food, liquor, try-your-luck stalls. Actors, performin' animals and tricksters of every kind. The monsters were just human and animal freaks. Humans with hands growin' out of their chests, that could draw your picture. Dwarves barely knee-high that used to race each other – one on a tiny horse, the other on a dog. A giant nigger-woman in the family way nursin' her husband – a tiny white Tom Thumb – on her lap. Withered hands and heads and noses in glass cases supposed to come from some famous king or queen. Unborn babies sucklin' a cow's udder in a jar. The feller who showed this lot used to go round the madhouses lookin' for freaks and even pick people out of the crowd if they were ugly enough. There was even a two-headed duck with three arseholes. A shaved monkey dressed as a fairy. Pigs with six legs. A tortoise with wings. And all sorts of rubbish like that. Most of them were real.

Rafferty hated anythin' unnatural. He said the human freaks should be put away, and the animals put to death. It disgusted him to see how so many people would pay to go and see these things. He would have walked fifty miles to see two angels fight if they were well matched. But he hated cruelty. And he detested seein' anythin' – man or animal – bullied or humiliated. The salamanders he didn't mind, although he didn't much fancy their job. Swallowin' needles and broken glass. Bitin' off the heads of live rats. Eatin' red hot coals and drinkin' lighted pitch and sulphur. My grandfather said their brains were as soft as their stomachs were hard. But at least they didn't do any harm to nobody but themselves. It was the way they went on with animals that spoiled the fairground life for my grandfather. Horses dancin' waltzes, wild beasts in cages, and things like firin' muskets with doves perched on the barrel. Fireworks fastened to donkeys' tails and dogs jumpin' through hoops of fire. It wasn't natural for animals to be unafraid of fire. And these sort of things sickened Rafferty.

He thought the actors were clever and that they had plenty of backbone. They used to bring more trouble upon themselves and the fairground than anythin' he ever saw. They would act out various events from the past and the present and make fun of local squires or judges by dressin' up to look like them and sayin' stupid things in their voices. This would make the people they were mimickin' a laughin' stock and when they heard about it they used to send in the constables and have the actors locked up as vagrants. The same thing would happen when they showed unjust executions of popular people – martyrs and the likes. They would rig everythin' up to make ye think somebody was actually bein' hung or havin' his head chopped off. When the constables came there'd be an almighty free-for-all with all the showmen and the flatties – non-showmen joinin' in. But most of the actors would escape till the next time. They never stayed around when the fists and sticks were flyin'.

All the showmen could turn their hands to a number of different things. They didn't just take money. They had to be able to perform. Jugglin', magic tricks, the slack rope. Anythin'. So that no matter how bad things were, they would always be able to make a few coppers. The winter was a dead time for them when they would have to take on labourin' jobs if they couldn't make enough from doin' tricks or singin' and dancin' in alehouses. As soon as the spring came, they would all get together again and back on the road. My grandfather remembered many a time when they had no money to cross a toll-bridge, and would have to give a little show there and then by the roadside.

All the fair bosses called themselves 'Lord this' or 'Sir that'. They were proper snobs and always thought themselves a cut above the rest. Even though they mightn't be bringin' in that much money they would always go to the auction sales to buy posh stuff. Many of them bankrupted themselves in this way. Clothes, furniture, carriages and trappin's. They used to bid the highest prices for somethin' that once belonged to a king

or a queen, or Napoleon. The front wagon was always covered
with carvin's and gildin'. It was often so big that it would
take thirty or forty horses to pull it. And the harnesses and
brasses were so heavy it would take an elephant to tow them.
The front wagon always had to have somethin' extra special
that would attract attention – like a beautiful girl dressed up
as Britannia with a real live lion chained to her ankle.

A dozen bandsmen done up in army uniforms from the
past would walk ahead of the train, covered in braid and
medals. Rafferty reckoned they could make more noise than
a whole regiment put together. The fair bosses used to organise
mock battles – like the Roman games – with chariot races and
the lot. These were popular for a while but Rafferty thought
they were a load of tripe and he wouldn't have anythin' to
do with the likes. They always ended up the same with the
English winnin' without scarcely ever losin' a man even though
they would be outnumbered ten to one. He preferred the
daft battles they had like when towers of men – maybe six
high all on each others shoulders – used to do a 'battle royal'.
There'd be as many as ten towers fightin' in the circus ring
at the same time. The man at the top would be all dressed
up like a gentleman with a top hat on, and the idea was for
all the top men to knock each other's hats off with a paper
rolled up into a truncheon. If ye had your hat knocked off, or
if your tower collapsed, then ye lost and the last tower still
standin' would be the winner. Bettin' was always heavy as to
the outcome. Mostly the towers were made up of gaff-lads
who loved a bit of rough and tumble fun like that. Of course
it wasn't just the top men who would be fightin' – although
that was the rules. Different ones in the middle of the towers
would be grapplin' with others to try and bring each other
down.

It was the good-naturedness and cheerfulness of the fair-
people that made Rafferty stay with them for so long. They
always had somethin' to occupy their minds with, and there
was plenty of hard work to keep a man fit.

After all the tents and stalls were up, Rafferty wouldn't have
so much to do so he had a little patch where he would do
strong-arm stuff. Eventually he saved enough money to buy

a small tent which he carried on his back. He would give boxin' exhibitions and lessons in physical culture. Three times every day he would do a spell on the wooden roundabouts, turnin' the handle for an hour or more to keep his strength up.

In 1855, Rafferty met a woman called Mary. She was small compared with him, but had lovely looks and a good head on her shoulders. She was the daughter of a master of the slack rope, and could do wonders up-a-height. She also had a great gift for bird sounds and could call the wild birds off the trees. They got married and the show-people did them proud. They bought Peter and Mary a hand-painted barrow for him to pull all their worldly goods around in from town to town. Both Rafferty and his wife walked everywhere. He said there was nothin' like it for stamina.

Rafferty had a friend called Sweeney, a feller from County Mayo. Sweeney was a tiger man and had been so all of his life, even though as a boy of seven he had been inside the cage when his father had put his head in a tiger's mouth and had it bitten clean off.

'I'll go the same way some day, Peter. Of that I'm certain. And it'll be the demon drink that'll do it. If ye stagger, drop on one knee, turn your back on them for a moment, or lose your concentration for a fraction, they'll have ye. That's why I go and have a listen to the preachers at the temperance tent. I'm tryin' to give it up.'

Whenever Sweeney was doin' an act, Rafferty would always be there watchin' if he wasn't givin' his own show. One night, Sweeney was badly drunk and stumbled. And they were straight on him. Three massive tigers. One ripped off an arm and started eatin' it. Another – a leg. The other one ripped open Sweeney's belly. By this time Rafferty was gone and back with two red hot irons from the blacksmithy. The owner of the wild beasts was standin' by, just watchin'. Sayin' nowt, doin' nowt.

'Get your gun and shoot the bastards!' yelled Rafferty.

'It's too late, Peter. He's had it. Those tigers are worth much more to me now than Sweeney is.'

Rafferty swung a poker across the neck of the owner who immediately went to the ground. He then slashed at the tiger that was still gorgin' the mangled body of Sweeney. It fell to the ground inside the cage. With the other, he speared the tiger. It tore round the cage as though it had gone mad, with the red hot poker still stickin' to it, smoulderin' and singein'.

'Don't go in, Peter,' said Mary. 'He's done for. Half his bowels are out. You can do nothin' for him now. You'll only get yourself killed. Wait till they've calmed down and we'll pull him out and give him a decent burial. We knew this had to happen some day. And so did Sweeney.'

In 1856, my grandfather and grandmother had a baby that was born dead. He was baptised and buried at the same time. Shortly after that, they were doin' a show near Chester and my grandfather and some of his friends went into an alehouse. When they came out, it was near midnight and they were immediately set upon by a press gang. They were outnumbered three to one and the pressmen were armed with cudgels and pistols. Rafferty had been laid out cold. By the time they were taken to Liverpool docks, Rafferty was awake though pretended not to be. Those of his friends who were on their feet were tied up with ropes. He wasn't. He was bein' half carried, half dragged along. He waited his chance. Apart from a lantern held by one of the gang, it was pitch dark. When they were half way across the gangplank, Rafferty, who had his arms round the shoulders of two of the gang, clashed their heads together and leaped into the water pullin' them with him. One drowned immediately but the other came up at the same time as Rafferty. Rafferty smashed his head against the side of the ship and down he sank like a stone. Rafferty then swam out across the river until he came to some steps.

Next day, on the way back to the fair, Rafferty had a big think to heself. He wasn't content with his boxin' booth. There were certain things he had to do to fit in with the wishes of the fair which made his show more like a circus than a place for carryin' on the manly arts. Mock-up fights annoyed him as did the fraud of gettin' two fully dressed men in the crowd who were supposed to be fightin', to come up on stage, and do it properly. It was all a big put-on. Women boxers and wrestlers did not please him either. And if the show was short and the crowd felt they hadn't had their money's worth,

Rafferty would have to fill in by bendin' iron bars or singin' and dancin'.

All this was settled soon, however, and it happened about in the followin' way. Rafferty despised the feller in charge of the performin' animals. Pigs that could read, horses that danced. Snakes that could tell the time and rabbits that could play the organ. This feller would feed sugar to horses and chocolates to dogs while his own kids went hungry. Rafferty felt it was better for animals to fight each other rather than be made to prance about like human fools. This particular afternoon, Rafferty had gone into the tent where this animal trickster was doin' his stuff, to fix a tent pole which had slipped. He was half way up the pole when he heard the audience laughin' like mad. When he looked down, he saw this feller had a donkey tellin' rosary beads. Rafferty slid down and hit the feller so hard in the mouth that he broke his jaw, and three of his teeth ended up stuck in Rafferty's fist. Rafferty then opened every cage and kicked this feller's dogs and rabbits out. Flung his bag of snakes into the crowd and let all his birds fly away. There was ructions on and the fair boss rushed in with his whip. He raised it to strike Rafferty but Rafferty grabbed it, snapped it, and then lifted the boss above his head and clashed him against the tent pole.

Rafferty told my grandmother that he was finished with the fair. 'Pack up,' he said, 'and we'll be gone.' They took down the booth and loaded it on the cart. As they were leavin', Mary's father came across with a mule.

'Here, Peter, you take it. It'll do to carry Mary and the bairn when it comes.' And that was that. From now on Rafferty and Mary were on their own. And that was the way he liked it best.

5
Prize-Fighting

Easter was comin'.

'Right, from now on, Mary, we're goin' to have a proper boxin' booth. One that I can be proud of. I've thought about it a great deal and know exactly what I want.'

Rafferty then hired cudgel-men, sword-masters and clog-fighters. These were to teach others and to fight amongst themselves. There was to be no more messin' around. Rafferty would see to the wrestlin' and bare-fist fightin' himself. In this way they travelled all over the country. When they had belonged to the fair, my grandfather and grandmother could only play in certain places. Fairs were frowned on by the law as they used to attract a lot of footpads and the like. Also they needed a lot of ground to put on the full show. But Rafferty could find space enough for his booth even in the smallest of towns and villages.

He would challenge anybody big or small, black or white. They got paid two shillings for goin' in with him for three rounds and anybody who could beat him would have got a crown extra. Rafferty had above twelve or fifteen fights a day on a good day and although the challengers weren't of his ilk, many of them could give a good account of themselves. This kept Rafferty very fit.

At thirty-five, Rafferty was in his prime. Proud, strong, hard, confident, mature. And full of charm. Always large-boned like a prehistoric animal, his flesh was now thicker. But without a trace of fat. His back was as straight as his hair. He never wore the beards, sidewhiskers or moustaches that were then in fashion. Mendoza had learned the bitter lesson of prize-fighters with long hair. Pugilism was unlegal, so open-air

fightin' was out on these occasions. But a covered tent and a
raised platform made it a boxin' exhibition and not a prize-
fight. And that was on the right side of the law – but only
just in most places. All around the tent were portraits of the
old greats. Broughton, Jackson, the Belcher brothers, Spring,
Donnelly, Corcoran and many others.

Standin' in front of the curtains which were parted enough
to show a roped stage, would be Rafferty, the Great Peter
Robinson. Mary would be sittin' smilin', lookin' beautiful in
her brightly coloured dress. At the side, ready to collect the
money. Rafferty would be all dressed up for the show. Legs
a yard apart. Soft, black leather shoes with elastic sides. Long,
narrow, striped trousers that strapped under his heels. A bright
green waistcoat buttoned right up. Stiff collar with turned
over edges and a silk cravat, tucked in in proper style. Grey kid
gloves to match the hand-made, long, grey frockcoat which
hung down to his knees. What a swell! And then ... a stiff,
dark brown, tall bowler with a wavy brim. He was seven foot
from top to bottom.

'Roll up! Roll up! Two silver shillin's to any man here who
seeks the privilege of tappin' the claret of Peter Robinson!'
He'd then rhyme off a couple of ditties about the bruisers of
old.

After he'd finished his spiel, Rafferty would bow and say,
'Lords and ladies, a gentleman for a gentleman?' Even though
he was a giant of a man, those who didn't know him would
be tempted, seein' as how he was dressed like a fop.

Somebody would shout, 'I'm no gentleman, but I'll knock
your hat off for a couple o' bob, Paddy, if that'll do ye!'
Rafferty would then bow deeper and more gracefully than
before and say, 'I may be a gentleman, sir, but I'm no snob.
I should deem it an honour to entertain you. Kindly step
through those curtains and prepare yourself.'

When the challenger had gone inside, Rafferty would then
carry on to get the crowd inside also. First, he'd draw the
curtains.

'Pardon me, I beg you, for bein' so vulgar as to undress in
front of you all but I should not wish to embarrass the good
gentleman's privacy.' He would jerk a thumb over his shoulder

at the feller gettin' changed inside the tent. Then he'd start, smilin' broader than ever. Mary would bring up a clothes-stand. First, off came the bowler to show a scalp of short black hair brushed straight from the crown to a fringe on his broad forehead. The hat he'd toss on to the top of the clothes-stand. He'd then glare fiercely at the crowd, his thick dark eyebrows joinin' up and his smile gone. People would look at each other and start murmurin'. Then Rafferty would smile again, then laugh out aloud and sing a verse of 'Molly Brannigan'. By the time he'd finished, Mary would be hangin' up his coat. As he carefully unbuttoned his waistcoat he'd be singin' the next verse. By the time the whole song was sung, Rafferty would be standin' stripped to the buff. He was magnificent! He'd have the whole crowd with him by now. He'd raise his hand to quell the cheerin'. 'If I still have your attention, Lords and Ladies, my modesty prevails upon me to doff my pants inside. I must crave your forebearance for a little while till I get my breeches and boots on. And then my good wife will graciously escort you into our little amphitheatre, for only threepence a head.' Who in the world could resist all that?

Soon 'Robinson's Boxing Booth' became well known and up-and-comin' fighters would flock to see Rafferty in action. Any that Rafferty thought good enough, he would train, but Rafferty would only take on the best men. It wasn't enough to want to fight. Ye had to be good before you came to him. He didn't care about size or looks. All that mattered was that ye could still stand after ten minutes with him. Everybody was up half an hour before first light. Rafferty taught fightin' accordin' to the old Jack Broughton rules, although he hadn't been brought up that way himself. His had been what they call 'Up and Down fightin''. In that style, when ye had a man down ye bloody well kept him down until he gave in. Broughton invented his rules to put a stop to eye gougin' and purrin' – kickin' a man in his precious parts when he was on the ground. Before Broughton drew up his rules, which were followed by most fighters of the day, everybody made up their own. There were far more deaths and far less sportsmanship. And very many more arguments.

So the rules were a good thing for the sport. Broughton

said that a square yard should be chalked out on a wood stage which was raised off the ground to stop everybody from pilin' in if things weren't goin' the way they wanted them to. The seconds had to bring their men up to the sidelines facin' each other for the set to. And if at any time a second couldn't bring his man up to scratch in half a minute of the other man, then that man had lost the contest. Both sides picked an umpire each. And if they couldn't agree on the outcome, then the umpires themselves picked a third who had to decide. When the battle was on only the fighters and their seconds were allowed on stage. Ye weren't to hit a man when he was on his back or even if he was down on one knee. And ye could no longer grab your opponent by any part of his body or clothes below the belt. The business of the knee wasn't all that good an idea because it came to be used as a dodge. If a man couldn't take any more punishment he could just drop on one knee and take a rest. But there again, whatever rules are brought in somebody will always find a way of twistin' them to his own benefit.

Broughton said that if everybody trained as a prize-fighter trains, every other shop would be a butcher's or a baker's instead of a chemist's or a doctor's. And if ye weren't properly trained, even though ye had spunk, muscle, strength and skill ye might as well whistle jigs to milestones as shy your castor over the ropes. Trainin' only means diet and exercise after all. My grandfather was very strict. Either ye obeyed or ye got out. And no in-betweens.

My father said Rafferty was a hell of a taskmaster and that was because of the way he had been brought up himself, in Ireland. When he had been trainin' for a big fight over there, in the 1840s, the squires would put him in the charge of trainers who were old champions themselves and knew all about the game. In them days ye always had to be sober and if ye felt ye must have a woman ye had to stick to one. Because she won't drain ye as much as a harem will. Ye were fed only when ye were hungry and ye drank only when ye were dry. That was the way to develop and keep your stamina – 'bottom' – as they called it in them days. Your skin should always be paler after trainin', but a tint of pink showed there was vigour in the constitution.

When the weather was fine he would be up before dawn, as soon as he 'woke. He believed that the openin' of the eyes is the sign to rise. First thing, Rafferty would have to wash hard with cold water till he glowed. Then he had to exercise to sweat the foulness out of his system. Next he had to scrub himself with warm water to open the skin right up and let every last drop of badness seep out. Then he had to close it again by douchin' in cold water. His strip had to be as fair as a woman's only pinker – ye can always tell a man's health by the condition of his skin. If he shivered, the sweatin' had to be stopped because shiverin' means your strength is sapped. Rafferty always used the flesh brush on himself, night and mornin', even long after the days when he was trained for a champion. He never exercised outside when it was damp but instead he did manly exercises indoors like sparrin', grindin' meal, or rubbin' down a horse or leap frog and ninepins. After that he was run hard for two miles and stopped only long enough to eat a crust before runnin' back.

He was allowed quarter of an hour for breakfast and then half an hour's rest to discuss pleasant things like fine battles and that to settle his mind and cheer him up. Then he had to start trainin' again. If he got thirsty in the middle of it he just had to dip his hands in cool fresh water. He did his heaviest sparrin' at noon or at the same hour as the contest was arranged for. His trainers would treat him with his opponent's manners and voice to get him prepared. After lunch he was permitted to rest for an hour. For the rest of the day they made him exercise really hard. Runnin', climbin', jumpin', swimmin', sparrin' – everythin'. By 7 o'clock he was in bed. A hard mattress with coarse linen and no curtains. His trainers watched over him all the while he slept. If they saw him breathin' quick and troubled, they drew the window up. But if he was seen smackin' his lips and wearin' a funny kind of smile, they pulled the window down. A man slumbers best when he can breathe in good health. If they thought that young Rafferty needed physickin', they gave him Joe Ward's three 3's. That was: three doses of salts, three sweats and three vomits. His victuals were never more than three-parts cooked. He wasn't given London-brewed liquor, but he wasn't denied his porter.

A pint a day was considered enough but if he wanted more he must never drink beer brewed by different breweries on the same day. And that's a good maxim for any man. If he fancied a drop of wine he got only best old port. If ever he was given tea or coffee, it was always clay cold. A fightin' man shouldn't need such stimulants. Rafferty's trainers were firm believers that water gruel was by far the best medicine in any dispensary and the greatest preventer of disease. Water gruel should be made from finest oatmeal, salt and water. And nothin' else. Never trust anybody but your trainer to make it. Ye aim for smoothness and thinness and ye must cook it slowly.

Young or white meat was held to be useless. And it still is. Fish pies and puddin's are poison to a fightin' man. Broil rump steaks and wether chops till the redness disappears. Use no fat and keep off the oily messes like gravy and batter. Exercise and hard work will digest any food. Only two big meals a day. Breakfast at 8 o'clock and dinner at 2 o'clock. No supper. Biscuits have a bad effect on the wind. Never eat bread unless it's been stale for at least two days.

That was the way my grandfather was trained when he was comin' on to fight and he never forgot any of it.

By this time, 1857, the London Prize-Ring Rules were bein' used for championship fights but my grandfather still stuck to the old rules of Jack Broughton. But he didn't agree with everythin' that Broughton preached. Broughton believed in bleedin' and cuppin' a man the day before his fight to tone down excitement. Rafferty believed in a cold bath. For purposes of teachin', Broughton brought in gloves – or 'mufflers' – so that gentlemen and the likes wouldn't get injured. Rafferty had no time for that either. He said that if ye were frightened of gettin' hurt, ye had no place in a fightin' ring.

6
Boru

When my grandparents' first kid was born dead, in 1856, I
don't think it bothered Rafferty so much as it did Mary – ye
know what women are about firstborns, especially their own –
no matter what they turn out like. Rafferty was well known
for his feelin's towards kids whether they were his or anybody
else's. But in this case it was different. This thing was so big
that my grandmother showed when she was only two months
gone. That was goin' to make trouble enough in itself. But
on top of that she'd went and fell from a high rope. At that
time her and Rafferty still belonged to the fair. Eventually it
was born before its time and when it came out its arms and
legs were all buckled and twisted. My grandfather said it was
better off dead. And that next time she'd have to keep off
the rope. And that was the end of that.

In the next year, 1857, they had another boy and this one
was all right. They called him Boru. By the time he was two
he was a fine strong lad and runnin' all over the place. In
some ways a travellin' fightin' show is maybe not the best
place for babies and the like. Not so much because of all the
travellin' – that'll do them no harm – but for the queer sorts
of people ye always get hangin' around any show.

Anyway a couple of years later, in 1859, the show had
been left in charge of my grandmother and a few tough
trusted men while Rafferty and the rest of his men had gone
to see Benjamin fight Tom Sayers for the championship at
Ashford. And to do some other business.

They were away for two weeks, and when they came back
Boru was missin'.

'What the hell's happened to him, woman? Where is he

for God's sake? What have ye done about it?' Rafferty took Mary by the throat and shook the daylights out of her.

'I don't know, Peter. I just don't know. I've searched everywhere for him. Everybody's helped me but we just can't find him anywhere. He just vanished last Thursday night. And there's been no sign of him since. Oh dear God, my poor little Boru. What's happened to him?' Mary was in an awful state about it. Anybody could see that. But that didn't bring Boru back, Rafferty's one and only son.

'You've no right to ask God, ye sinner. He gave him to you to look after! And so did I!'

'I've been to all the churches in the parish and to the poor-houses but they don't know anything. And I daren't go to the law because of the old trouble. I'm sure he hasn't drowned or anything because we've been to the river umpteen times and he's not there. And there's only two ponds for miles around and Mick and Jonah have dived in and swam all along the bottom, looking. Haven't you, Mick?'

'Yes, Peter. I'm certain nothin' like that's happened to him.'

'Get out of the way! Come here, you stupid bitch! I'm goin' lookin for him. And if I come back without him, you're done for!'

'Do you want something to eat first, Peter? It won't take me a minute to heat something up for you.'

'Eat? Eat!! Make your last confession, ye worthless slut, ye!'

Mary was not of Rafferty's breed. Strong enough for a woman, yes. Tough enough to stick the circus life, yes. But of a different ilk altogether to Peter Rafferty. No man was a match for Rafferty. And when he was in a rage – which, thank God, wasn't often – everybody got well out of his way. Because it was for sure somebody's head would get broken. Mary was a quiet woman, a gentle woman. An educated woman. A kind-hearted woman. A lovin' woman. The kind of woman that Rafferty liked. But if she could get her own bairn lost, she was no mother at all and not fit for a wife either. It was no use makin' excuses to Rafferty about havin' too much to do to look after his son. She loved the boy as well. My father always said she was a good mother, but, it's all very well to talk. Boru was gone, and the best thing she could do would be to get to hell out of it before Rafferty got back. But if she went, and Rafferty came back with the kid, then he'd be madder than ever. If Boru was found, Peter would forgive her, she knew that. And if he wasn't found, then she deserved all she had comin' to her.

All the fellers that had been away with Rafferty came to help to look for Boru. And away they went with Rafferty in the lead. They searched fields, forests, rivers, farms, ponds, quarries, and disused buildin's for miles and miles around. They kicked on doors, stopped travellers, went to poorhouses, churches. Everywhere they could think of. Rafferty dropped everythin' else for two whole weeks. Some of the men got fed up lookin' after the first week and just drifted away. One had to tell my grandfather in a friendly way that it was no use now, that they would never find Boru alive. But Rafferty had struck him so hard that they couldn't revive him for over two hours. So nobody else said nowt. They just quietly went about the business of lookin'. By the end of the second week Rafferty's temper had got so bad that the only one who dared stay with him was Mick. He worshipped my grandfather and stuck by him even though, like the others, he was completely worn out. They hadn't had a cooked meal in all that time. Just raw turnips, potatoes or anythin' else they could lay their hands on and eat without stoppin'. Even Rafferty must have realised how hopeless it was because eventually he went back to the camp. When he got there, Mary had gone. The others had told her he was on his way back. And that he was ravin' mad. When he came he didn't even call her name. No one told him. He knew she wouldn't be there. And he didn't expect her to be either. The camp just stayed where it was and the show went on even though Rafferty took no part in it. Not that he just sat around mopin'. Not him. He was out from first thing in the mornin' till yon time at night. Searchin' and searchin'. All day and every day – I suppose it would seem funny to people today to think that a rough and violent giant of a man like him would concern himself so much over a two-year-old kid. But that's the way he was. Anyway, one night Mary came into the camp carryin' the little Boru. He was covered in thick, crusty sores.

'He was filthy dirty when I found him, Peter. I washed him in a stream on the way back. He's starving, poor bairn. Some beggars had him. But before you say anything I must tell you that they were very loving towards him. They didn't steal him. He must have wandered off and then been picked up by some travellers who passed him on to these beggars. One of them was suckling him as well as her own bairn to make sure he got some nourishment. And you couldn't get anybody kinder than that. Making their own bairn suffer for a stranger. But he's covered in these awful sores. I've never seen anything like them before.'

Rafferty looked at the poor, miserable woman holdin' her bairn to her breast. Her beautiful hair filthy and tangled. Her face white with hunger and her eyes red with weeks of weepin'. Her hands smaller and thinner than he had ever seen them. She was shakin'. He put his great arm around her.

'Hush. Go clean him and feed him. Get him well. Then tend to yourself.'

After that he said no more on the matter.

At first, the kid seemed to pick up after a few days. But after that he went down and down. They had him to quack doctors, ordinary doctors and chemists. But none of them did any good. When he lost the use of his legs, Rafferty carried him on his back wherever he went. Sometimes Boru got a bit better and sometimes he got a bit worse. Rafferty said that when they next met up with the gypsies they would put him right. If they couldn't cure him nobody could. So when Rafferty heard that there was a big gypsy camp about forty miles away, off he went. He came back two days later with three gypsies. On a horse he had borrowed off them. He was told that the kid had taken a turn for the worse and that Mary and him were stayin' at a doctor's place in the village.

Rafferty told the gypsies to follow him. And all four galloped off at top speed. When my grandfather found the house where Mary and the kid were stayin', he belted up the stairs. The little mite was lyin' on a sheet with nowt on. All over his body there were steamin' jars. In between these were bunches of fat leeches. Some were so bloated they had dropped off and were squirmin' away, all purple. Boru was just lyin' there starin' up at the ceilin'. Two huge black eyes in a sunken little head. As Rafferty rushed to the bed, two well dressed but scruffy doctors tried to stop him from touchin' his own son. Rafferty shoved them aside and brushed off all the leeches. Then he screwed the jars off. As they came off with a plop they left big high red rings all over the kid's body.

'What on earth do you think you're doing, you lunatic! You're interfering with our treatment. And take your hands off those leeches. They're worth a lot of money.'

As Rafferty rolled the kid up in the sheet the doctors demanded that he pay their bills before he left the premises.

'Bills? Bills! You bloody swines have drained all the sap out of the poor little soul.'

With that, he took one of the doctors and threw him clean through the window and out into the street. Then he grabbed a handful of leeches and squashed them into the face of the other doctor. And at the same time he rammed the back of his head against the wall. The doctor fell in a heap on the floor, completely out. Rafferty and Mary left, carryin' Boru in his arms. Outside, the gypsies were waitin'. They all raced back to the camp. But when Rafferty got down from his horse and pulled aside the cover he could see that Boru was already dead.

7

Fighting Dogs

By 1859 baitin' was supposed to be banned but although ye never saw lions, bears or mad monkeys any more, if ye kept your eyes and ears open ye could still find the odd game bull.

Scroggins, the father of the fightin' dog that Rafferty now owned, had had so much pluck that when Rafferty heard of a bull ring in Cumberland where he was travellin' at the time, he decided to try him. Scroggins was forty-five pounds of muscle and bone and was a cross between a bulldog and a mastiff. Although he wasn't as nimble as the Staffordshire terrier, he had a hell of a grip. And once he sank his teeth in he would have hung on even if ye'd cut his legs off. And some doggers did just that if the stakes were high enough.

This particular bull was an old hand at the game and was as crafty as he was tough. The bull was staked to a fifteen-yard rope fastened to its horns. Rafferty paid the bullot – the owner – two shillin's for a run at his bull. The idea was for the dog to run 'far and fair'. That meant it had to tackle the bull straight from the front without dodgin' about like a knave on the run. Although Scroggins had never been matched against a bull before, he was clever and knew just what to do. So did the bull. It pawed a hole in the ground to protect its head because it knew the dog would go for its eyepiece or its nose, its lips or its tongue. Scroggins got right down on his belly and eased along the ground, flat as a snake. When he was no more than a foot from the bull he had leaped at its head. Quick as a flash the bull up with his horns and tossed Scroggins thirty feet into the air. Rafferty ran underneath him to catch him on his shoulders. That was allowed. But all he had managed to do was to break the dog's fall because Scroggins' belly had been slit open and he slithered down Rafferty's shoulders with his guts hangin' out. Those that had bet on the bull cheered and went to collect their bets.

'Hold it!' says Rafferty. 'He hasn't even started yet. That was just a warm up.'

He had took off his leather belt, shoved the dog's entrails back inside its belly, wrapped it twice round and buckled it up.

'Here,' he said, tossin' another two bob bit in the ring. 'Give him another go.'

This time Scroggins had stuck closer to the ground draggin' blood and slime after him. When he had got up to six inches off the bull's head, he lay stock still and never blinked an eye. The dog eyed the bull and the bull eyed the dog. And neither made a move. Steam was comin' out of the bull's nose.

'C'mon, Robinson,' shouted the men. 'Let's have some action.'

'Quiet,' says Rafferty. 'Leave him be. He knows what he's about.'

Suddenly the dog growled and the bull immediately lifted his head. Scroggins was straight at him. His teeth were deep in the bull's nose and blood squirted out all over the place. The bull jumped up and tossed and clashed Scroggins at the ground but he wouldn't let go. After five minutes of this the bull gave up and stood limp with Scroggins still hangin' from his nose.

'All right, Robinson. The dog wins,' said the bullot. 'Choke him off.'

'He won't choke off now,' said Rafferty.

'Then break his bloody jaw with this,' said the bullot, tossin' Rafferty a stave.

'Like hell I will,' said Rafferty steppin' in to the ring. He pulled a knife from his trousers and hacked a slice from the bull's nose. Scroggins fell to the ground and Rafferty put him in a sack and threw it over his back.

'Why, you Irish bastard. You've cut his bloody nose off. The flies'll get him now.'

'That's your look-out, mister. Maybe he's ready for makin' steaks now.'

Everybody had laughed except the bullot. Even those who'd lost their money. They used to say that a coursed hare or an animal which had extended itself was better eatin' than one which had been slaughtered.

'It takes a fightin' man to keep a fightin' dog,' says the bullot.

'Aye, and same goes for those who keep fightin' bulls,' said Rafferty, takin' off his waistcoat.

'You're a big feller, Robinson. Let's see if your heart's as big as your gin trap.'

They had peeled off to the buff and the crowd once again laid their bets.

'Here we wrestle,' says the bullot. 'Draw the line, Jackie.' Jackie took the stave used for prisin' dogs' jaws apart, and marked out a line.

The bullot was big and burly but carried too much fat.

Rafferty threw him again and again. The bullot was far too slow.

'Stay down or give in,' said Rafferty. 'You're beat.'

'You'll have to cut my throat before I'd give in to a Shamrock.'

As the bullot stumbled to his feet for the fourth time, Rafferty hit him so hard in the ear that blood gushed out and the whole of the side of his face went black. The bullot went down and stayed down. Rafferty picked up his winnin's and his sack and walked off.

'Serve's the bugger right,' said one bloke who ran after Rafferty. 'That bloody bull once ran mad and killed my brother. Trampled him to death it did. And that swine said it was his own fault for gettin' in the way.'

'Oh,' says Rafferty. 'Well, maybe it was at that.'

So much for Scroggins. He was long since dead now. The blowflies had got him in the end. He was such a game dog that he had worried three bitches to death while he was actually knotted up with them. But before he died, my grandfather had got him mated with a champion bull-terrier bitch and from that pairin' came Deaf Burke. Usually if a dog was any good at all it would fight to kill at three months. Deaf Burke showed that kind of spirit at two months, and Rafferty prized this dog. He trained it as hard as he trained any of his men. Dog-fighters were much like prize-fighters. It was the gameness that counted more than the winnin'. Greens, raw meat and cow's foot jelly. Good for man and dog alike. Dogs can only sweat through their paws and their tongue, particularly their tongue. So if a dog was out of condition or carryin' too much fat and its tongue lolled out, the other dog would grab it and that would be the end of the matter.

Rafferty would train his dogs with a branch. When the dog had sunk its teeth in, Rafferty would tie it up and then jerk the stick to toughen up the dog's jaws and strengthen the muscle in its neck and back. He said the best way to fit a dog for fightin' was to wean it in the rat pit. The rat pit was another place where the sportsmen used to gather to lay their bets.

Here the game was to see how quick the dog could nail

the rats. You could match a lightweight dog against a heavy-weight because the reckonin' was that for every extra pound of dog an extra rat should be put away, in the same time. So, if a twenty-pound dog killed 100 rats in ten minutes, a forty-pounder would have to do in 121 rats to win. And in ten minutes as well. Like with baitin' and fightin', it was often the skill of the setter – the dog's second – which won the match.

Deaf Burke did all that was expected of him in the rat pit. He would attack anythin' that moved from a mouse to a mule. And became so famous that whenever Rafferty and his booth arrived in a new town, in no time at all somebody would come up with a challenge. Once, when Rafferty had put up his booth in Penrith, a stagecoach full of dog-fighters and gamblers came all the way from Kendal to match the local champion dog against Deaf Burke. The arrangements were drawn up and the bets laid. The fight was to take place in a barn on the moor, and hundreds gathered on the Sunday mornin'. One thing about fightin'-dogs, they made no noise, but the backers and dog-players made plenty.

A dog pit was already set up and the chalk lines made by the time Rafferty, Deaf Burke, and his followers arrived. The pit was about fifteen feet across and was surrounded by a three-foot-high wooden wall. Some dog owners hired seconds to play their dogs, but Rafferty played his own.

Rafferty and the other dog's owner each paid the taster a shillin' to check their dogs. The taster's job was to lick the coat of the dogs to make sure that no poison or corrosive had been rubbed in. The other dog, Stevenson, was a reachey – that meant it attacked downwards. It was a big brown bull-terrier bitch. And a good dog.

The rules were as usual. The dog that failed to come up to scratch, lost. When a dog let go its hold or turned up, the round would end. One minute was allowed between rounds to sponge the dogs and to give the dog which had cried off in the last round time to cross the chalk-line into the other dog's half. Both dogs were weighed in at thirty-eight pounds. The coin was tossed and the fight began.

After an hour and a half, sixteen rounds had been fought and Deaf Burke had killed the other dog. This ended the round. But to win, Deaf Burke had to come up to scratch for the seventeenth round even though Stevenson was dead. That was the rules. Deaf Burke's backers went mad. But Rafferty couldn't get the cur to come up to scratch in time and the dead dog won the match. Rafferty grabbed Deaf Burke by the scruff and drowned him in the water butt. That was the way to treat curs and everybody expected it. That was why there was always a water butt handy at every dog-job.

8

Fighting Cocks

In the winter of 1860, Henry Robinson, my father, was born in Blackfriars. And in the spring of 1862, John Robinson, my uncle, was born in Driffield. Henry was always called 'Harry' and John, 'Johnny'. Their births were never registered because of the trouble their father, Rafferty, had been in. Although Harry and Johnny always used Robinson, in the family we always called my grandfather 'Rafferty' or 'Big Peter'. My father always referred to his own father as 'Big Peter' and nothin' else. The past was best forgotten.

Rafferty and my grandmother continued travellin' around with their booths and the two boys grew up amongst blood.

When Harry was seven years old and Johnny five, Rafferty bought them a Knowsley fightin'-cock each. He didn't bother too much with the birds himself but he knew it would be an important part of his travellin' fightin' show. Men, dogs and gamecocks. The two boys would be pitted against each other even though Harry was much bigger than Johnny. This used to bring the crowds in to see the rest of the sportin' entertainment. When Ann, my aunt, was born she also helped with the fightin' animals. Her job was to feed them and clean them out.

Harry's cock was called 'Cribb' and Johnny's was called

'Tinman'. They would be matched against all-comers and the bettin' would be as heavy as it was on the dogs or the fightin'-men. The birds had been specially picked by a friend of Rafferty's who was a cockmaster and knew all about fightin'-cocks. By the time the birds were two years old, they had huge thighs and proud scarlet heads. A red head shows that a bird has lust, strength and spine. The cockmaster friend showed the two boys how to dub their birds – cut their wattles off – and how to get them ready for a fight. Four days before a fight the birds had to be fed only old manchet at sunrise, noon and sunset, and were given only the coldest, sweetest spring water that could be found. Manchet was white bread. Different cockers had their own secret recipes. Some would add liquorice, aniseed or spices to heat the cock up. Rafferty's friend had his own special recipe and he used to add bruised caraway seeds, best white wine, wood-sorrel, ground ivy and dandelion to his mixture. When it was baked ye always soaked it in a strong man's pee before givin' it to the bird to eat. Its flesh had to be firm but corky.

If your bird was carryin' too much glut and grease he had to be sweated and scoured. If this was the case, first ye took a dunghill cock and showed him to your gamecock. Ye had to carry the dunghill cock on your arm and get the gamecock to chase ye till it panted, then ye took him to the cockhouse and forced butter mixed with hyssop and rosemary down his throat. Then ye stove him in a covered basket with soft straw beddin'. Ye repeated this every day till ye got the cock the way you wanted him. The day before the fight, they were starved to put a keen edge on their spirit. If the bird was good and in pink condition ye could tell his spirit by the way he strutted, the way he treaded, and by the way he crowed.

Ye had to pluck out all bloody or broken feathers and sharpen the quills on his wings. At the same time ye trimmed his bottom beak so that he would be able to get a good hold with his top beak. He should end up lookin' like an eagle. Ye pulled out most of the feathers on the crown of his head, and just before the contest, rubbed spittle into it to prevent the other bird from gettin' a good grip. But ye had to leave sufficient feathers on his crown to allow a fair hackle.

If ye were usin' gaffles, then the round, razor-edged ones were the best. That way the fight will always have a fatal conclusion. Steel or silver spurs make quick clean wounds which heal quickly, but nickels are deadly. They don't heal properly at all. So ye must always check the other bird's spurs to see what they're made of. Naked-heel fightin' can last two hours or more. If the terms of the fight said ye weren't allowed to use gaffles, then ye had to sharpen his own spurs with a knife on the mornin' of the fight. A two-year-old bird's spurs should be at least three inches long. It didn't pay to put poison on your spurs because the other feller always had the right to make ye lick your own spurs before the contest started.

A bird that had been trained to strike at the head and throat had a better chance of winnin' than a stronger bird which only attacks the body. To train them ye blooded the head and throat of the sparrin' partner and fitted hots – soft leather gloves – to cover the spurs.

The fights were usually arranged between cockers from different towns. This meant there would be a score or so fights and each town had its own main of cocks. Sometimes they would have a 'battle-royal' where a dozen cocks would be put in the cockpit together. There were also Welsh-mains and knockout events. And usually there was a shakebag contest where ye didn't declare the weight or size of your cock to the other feller until the bets were laid. Then when the signal was given, both cockers emptied their shakebag cocks out of a sack and the battle would begin. At the start of any battle the first thing ye had to do was to tease your cock till it went wild. Then usually ye set your cocks beak to beak and the survivor, or the one which came to scratch at the finish, was the winner. When the birds sagged, they were separated and after a count of ten they were set to again. If a beaten cock failed to come up to scratch after a count of forty, it lost. Odds were always changin' as first one bird was throated and then the other. My father says it was sometimes impossible to tell which way a battle was goin' because there was so much blood about ye couldn't see which was which.

After the battle, if your cock survived, ye would straight-away suck his wattles to prevent ramblin' and then wash

them with warm pee. There was always eye wounds. To check
them ye chewed the juice of ground ivy and then spat it into
the cock's eye. Hare-down was the best thing for stoppin'
bleedin'. If there were still any septic lumps after a month
ye had to cut them open with a knife and suck out the corruption and then fill the holes up with fresh butter. Although
many people said that dog-fights were the gamest, my father
says that of the three sports, gamecock-fightin' was the bloodiest,
then prize-fightin' and least of all dog-fightin'.

In 1870 when my father, Harry, was just turned ten,
Rafferty matched him against a dog in the rat pit. Because
when Harry was a boy, although he was a big lad, he was
very quick and light on his feet. My grandfather used to teach
him to kill rats comin' out of haystacks to build up his speed
and to give him an alert eye. Rafferty would stand at one
end of the haystack and Harry at the other, and Harry'd be
crouchin' legs apart with a hazel in either hand. When he
gave the signal that he was ready, Rafferty would welt his
side of the stack and the rats would come teemin' out. Then
Rafferty would come runnin' round to Harry's side to see
what was goin' on and to clout him for every rat he missed.
Mind, there was no messin' about. My father could break a
rat's back by a kick from either foot or a single swipe with a
stick. He never wounded. They were always killed outright.

This pit that Harry was to do battle in was about eight feet
high and fifteen feet across. Harry and the dog were to be
given forty rats apiece. And the one who put away their rats
in the shortest time, won. A broken back didn't count as a
kill unless it couldn't pass the dinner-plate test. That was
where ye drew a chalk circle the size of a dinner plate around
the wounded rat. Then ye smacked its tail with the edge of
a butter pat. If it crawled out of the circle it was counted
as still bein' alive. If it couldn't or didn't, that counted as a
kill even though it might still be squealin'.

A good dog would kill a hundred rats in ten minutes easy.
To start off, what ye did was to wait till the rats were all in
a bunch, and then ye dropped your dog in. The moment he
hit the ground the clock would be set. The dog should then
straightaway get started on the rats. It had to waste no time

shakin'. Just grab it, bite it and drop it. Then move on to the next one. And so on. In this particular contest, the dog, Wilson, disposed of his rats in four minutes. Two kills were disputed but were found to be genuine after the dinner-plate test had been done on them. When it came to my father's turn his two sticks were taken off him by the umpires after Wilson's mob complained it was unfair for him to use anythin' other than his natural weapons.

'All right, then,' said Rafferty. 'If that's the way ye want it. Right son, jump in when you're ready and show these buggers what ye can do.'

So Harry jumped in and lashed about with his big leather boots. Unlike when the dog was in, the rats went flyin' everywhere. Some of them clean out of the pit and into the crowd. But it took him nearly five minutes to finish them off, and so he lost. Even so the spectators cheered like mad. It was completely different to what they'd been used to. And as Harry stood in the centre of the pit, surrounded by forty dead rats with his arms above his head, the coppers poured into the pit, chucked in by winners and losers alike.

But all this stuff with dogs and rats and birds meant little to Rafferty. It was business, it was entertainment. Nowt else. But as far as the boys Harry and Johnny were concerned, it showed them what fightin' was all about. That to compete with the best ye had to be perfectly fit and trained to a hair. And to win ye had to take everythin' and give more. Never quit. If ye couldn't stand, ye couldn't hear, or ye couldn't see, let somebody else put a stop to it. For the energy it costs to toss in your own towel could be used instead to deliver a last defiant blow. There was no shame in losin' if ye fought like a man and gave your all. To the last ounce. When Harry and Johnny were fightin' each other, or anybody else, they never dared give in. They would always hear their father's boomin' voice, 'Go down if ye must, ye weaklin', but don't any of ye step back!'

Harry was so much bigger and stronger than Johnny that it made Johnny quicker, cleverer and harder. At the end of a fight, my grandfather would sit them down and he would attend to them himself. Washin' the blood from their faces with brine and pretendin' not to notice the odd tear in their eye. After they'd rested and he'd been tellin' them what they'd done wrong and how well they were comin' on – as the case may be – he'd piss into a bucket and Johnny and Harry would stick their fists into it. Then he'd say:

'Now listen to me, lads. Don't get disheartened because ye didn't come off best today. There always has to be a winner and there always has to be a loser. But there's never need for a coward. By the time I'm finished with yous, ye'll win all your fights because there'll be nobody good enough to beat ye. I deliberately pit ye against bigger and tougher lads but there's none truly better than yous two. You, Harry, or you, Johnny. I know that. But ye'd learn nowt and I'd disgrace us all if I matched ye with men who were less than you are, or who were only as good. But one day ye'll find I cannot find your better. When that time comes, others will try. Sometimes they'll come up with somebody. Then the day will come when nobody can. And that'll be the day when you're grateful to me. In the meantime, remember this. Let him hit ye. Let him break his fist on your head. Then double him up! But at all times respect your man. If ye don't, he's not worth fightin'. Don't take your shirt off to any man. You're fighters, not brawlers. Keep your skills for the real men. Ignore the stupid buggers who'd drag ye down just because you're better than they are. Those who scrap in the streets and bars are fools. They fight only in gangs like cowards and lynchers. If your pride's hurt, offer them the chalk. Do it properly. See how many are prepared to take ye on fair and square with a crowd watchin'. That's the real test of a man.

'When a man has no fight left in him he's ready to die. And if he wasn't born with any, he shouldn't have been born at all. A well-matched opponent in a ring only wants to beat ye, he doesn't want to murder ye. And when defeat is conceded, he'll pat your back and help ye up and wish ye better luck for next time. If he hears you're in a bad way, like as not he'll come and enquire after ye. That's what I call a man. A worthy opponent.

'Right. I can see ye smilin' at each other again. Good. Now shake hands on it and remember this. Lose your composure in a fight and you've had it. And if ever I catch either of ye losin' your temper in a ring, I'll step in and thrash ye meself. There and then. Understand? Keep that little cool tantalisin' smile on your face from the moment ye get in to the moment ye get out. Everybody'll like ye for it and ye'll be half way there before ye even start.

'Now go on get yourselves smartened up and get about your jobs. I want you to change them ropes, Harry. And Johnny, you see to the dogs.'

Rafferty would then stand up on his thick muscular legs, take a deep breath into his massive lungs and lower his huge arms. He'd look at his boys with his strong, hard face. His black head cropped and his waistcoat open. Great dusty boots a yard apart. He'd unclench his fists and fill his baggy pockets with his hands. Harry and Johnny would walk away and look back at him to see him grinnin' like Galway Bay.

9

Harry and Johnny

By 1871 my grandmother wanted Rafferty to settle. Harry was now eleven, Johnny was nine, and Ann was eight.

For the past year or two Mary's health had been failin'. The hard life on the road, out in all weathers, and the long hours with the booths. Sometimes she went for days without proper meals. And whenever they got a good spot that drew the crowds, word would get round. Rumours would follow them wherever they went. They didn't bother Rafferty but Mary would always be fearin' for his safety. And he was always gettin' into trouble because of prize-fightin', or the dogs, or the cocks. All of it beyond the law. She had been pleadin' with him for years to give it up. For his sake. For the children's. And now for her own as well. She was forever

c

gettin' chills and had once nearly died after a fever caught
in the mountains of lakeland. A place which Rafferty loved.
It was quiet, it was wild, and the people loved the fightin'
sports. Anyway, Rafferty eventually agreed. My grandmother
had managed to save a bit of money by this time. She looked
after the money because Rafferty gambled away everythin'
he laid his hands on. They decided to buy a lodgin' house
in Hartlepool and Mary Robinson's name went up as proprietor. Mary was to look after the lodgin' house and Rafferty
would go about his own business. He got rid of all the dogs
and cocks. And shortly after, the booth had to go as well. It
was attracting too much attention.

Lodgin' houses were really catchin' on then. People moved
about a lot lookin' for jobs, and workin' on contracts. So long
in one place till the job was finished, then off somewhere else.
Railways, roads, bridges, buildin's. There was always somethin' goin' on. These people were good payers. They couldn't
afford to stay in inns like in the old days and if they stayed
in shanty camps or hostels they had to live like pigs and be
cheated at the tommy shops. Twopence a night. In a place
like Hartlepool, my grandmother had regulars she could rely
on. People who belonged to the town. Also there were always
plenty seamen ready to take any spare beds. So she would
never have any trouble gettin' her beds properly filled. She
could make meals for them if she wanted to, or wash their
clothes. A bit darnin' here a bit sewin' there. All for a few
extra coppers. Soon, things were goin' well.

But after a couple of years of this my grandmother started
ailin' again and often had to take to her bed. She tired too
easy. But Ann was very strong and a good worker. She
carried the lodgin' house, doin' all the scrubbin' and cleanin'.
My grandmother still did the shoppin' and looked after the
takin's and did whatever light jobs she could. When the
booth went, so did Rafferty. He took more and more to goin'
away. For weeks at a time. Always takin' his two boys with
him. All three of them would do navvyin' jobs to keep them
tough and they would eat and sleep outdoors, leavin' Ann
and my grandmother to run the lodgin' house on their own.
Neither Harry or Johnny got schoolin' in anythin' but fightin'.

There was not much else they could do. Ye had to pay to
learn a trade. And even then what ye got was next to nowt.
There were hundreds of men out of work. Strikes in the mines,
strikes in the buildin's. Strikes everywhere. Men were tryin'
to get more money and better conditions to work in. And
the Government were bringin' in foreigners – Belgians, Ger-
mans and them sorts to work in their place. Naturally this
caused a lot of trouble. People were always killin' themselves.
Stringin' themselves up or cuttin' their own throats. There
was terrible accidents every day of the week. Young lads
gettin' their heads crushed by tubs or bein' blown up in the
mines. Factory-girls gettin' their hands cut off by machines
and fellers gettin' scalded to death in vats of hot liquid-lead
in the shotten works. So prize-fightin' was the best job for my
father and Uncle Johnny. And anyway that's what they were
cut out for.

In those times everybody seemed to be occupied with their
health. At least the rich ones anyway. They would be forever
fillin' their bellies with all sorts of foreign muck one minute
and then worryin' about how to get rid of the troubles it
caused the next. There was plagues of the pox all over. First
here, then there, then here again. But that was mostly amongst
the poor people. Consumption seemed to go for anybody,
rich and poor alike. The rich would hire doctors for the
slighest little thing and these fellers did a roarin' trade. German
foot-doctors who charged 2s 6d for removin' bunions and
corns. Imagine that, mebbes two days' pay just to have your
foot attended to. And if ye hadn't the money, ye'd had it.
Ye kept your corns and your aches and pains to yourself. One
bloke was walkin' along the street this day when he saw a
fight that was goin' badly for one of the parties. He stepped
in to put a stop to it and his head was split open by a brick.
Somebody took him to a doctor's nearby because he was
bleedin' badly. But because he couldn't pay, the doctor
wouldn't do anythin' for him, not even to stop the bleedin'.
The doctor said he'd have to go to the Infirmary. On the
way there the poor bloke collapsed and bled to death in the
street. The dispensaries used to sell all sorts of pills and
medicine but these were far too dear for anybody who wasn't

well off. The poor people had to rely on the quacks and their poison if they could afford it.

Rafferty got fed up with all this. He had never lived in a town in his life. He loved travellin'. Meetin' different people and movin' when and where he felt like it. He was used to bein' with fit, active people. A different sort altogether to the ones ye get in towns. Mopin' on street corners or spendin' all their time arguin' in bars. All this smoke and moanin' and sickness. If Rafferty was hungry he wouldn't starve to death in a midden. He wouldn't go beggin' to the workhouse. He'd go out into a field and catch a rabbit or a sheep. He wouldn't ask either. He'd just kill it and eat it and wash it down with a drink of fresh water. It was all free to him. He showed Harry and Johnny how to go on. How to get into mischief and how to get out of it.

But all the time the fightin' was in him. He could never get enough of it. If he couldn't find anybody for his own lads to fight, he took them both on himself. First Harry and then Johnny. And sometimes both at once. They would get work on a farm doin' the heaviest labourin' work they could find. And afterwards the three of them would run for miles and miles. Swimmin' rivers, climbin' hills, jumpin' fences. Chasin' and racin' horses, dogs and hares. Punchin' sacks of grain till their hands bled. Peein' on them till the bleedin' stopped, and then the same again next day. Till Harry and Johnny could punch anythin' without breakin' skin. Whenever Rafferty heard of a good fight in the district, he'd take the boys to see it and before the big contest started he would make them both get up in the ring to offer their challenges to the crowd. Always the boys fought men. And mostly they won. But even if they didn't, they were never disgraced.

The three of them were very close to each other. Though whether it was more fondness than respect, I don't know. It's certainly easier to hit a man ye respect than one ye like. And it's hard to love a man who smashes his fist in your face every day of the week. Somethin' has to go. And both Harry and Johnny each tried to prove to their father that they were the best. None of them had their father's charm. Ye couldn't knock it out of Rafferty, but I think that from a very early

age Harry and Johnny lost theirs. Harry was big and dark
after his father. Johnny, slim and fair like his mother. Harry
had the strength, Johnny the speed. But Rafferty was bigger,
stronger and better than the two of them put together. He
always had them dressed in knee-breeches and sarks. Necker-
chiefs. No jackets. Rafferty still wore his frockcoat. Over a
green waistcoat that wouldn't button. Gone the old fairground
bowler. Three cropped heads. Three pairs of stitched boots.
Somewhere, two big boys and a very big man walked to Mass
every Sunday.

Peter Rafferty hated liars like he hated top-hats. One day he
came into the barn where him and the boys were livin' at the
time. He looked around, nodded to Harry and Johnny and
then hung up his coat on a butcher's hook that was stuck in a
beam.

'Who told you ye could wear my belt, Johnny?'

'I was just tryin' it on, Dad.'

'Who told you ye could wear my belt!'

'Me mother said I could wear it sometimes, Dad.'

'Then you're a liar as well as a fool. Take it off and I'll
show ye what a good belt it is. Don't squeal. I'll decide when
you've had enough.'

He thrashed Johnny till the tears came to Harry's eyes.
The next day, after the work was done Rafferty came back
to the barn.

'Johnny.'

'Yes, Dad.'

'You know where I got this belt?'

'Yes, Dad.'

'Where?'

'Gypsy Mungalo, Dad.'

'Still want the belt, Johnny?'

'Yes, Dad. It's a good belt.'

'Want to try conclusions for it?'

'Ye mean with you, Dad?'

'I'm givin' ye the chance to prove you're man enough to
wear it.'

'I've got no choice, have I?'

'Not now ye haven't, son. Take your shirt off. Harry, get the chalk.'

Three times Rafferty knocked Johnny down. Every time Johnny got up again and put his fists up to his father.

'Had enough, lad?'

'No, Dad.'

'Still want the belt?'

'Yes, Dad.'

'Here,' says my grandfather, unbucklin' it and tossin' it across. 'You've deserved it. But don't ever try to take anythin' from me again. Next time ye won't get it so easy. I don't like your cheek, Johnny, but I admire your spunk. Anythin' ye want Harry?'

'No, thanks, Dad. I'd settle for your fiddle. But not after ye'd brayed is with it first.'

'When ye show me ye can play a jig faster than I can, it's yours, lad.' They both laughed. Johnny quietly picked the belt up and put it on.

One day the three of them had taken a young bull and killed it. They were in the middle of cuttin' it up when this squire rode up with three of his men. Two of the men were pointin' guns.

'Want a slice?' says Rafferty.

'Come with me!' says the squire. 'Walk ahead of my horse where I can see you. If you try to run, I'll have you shot.'

'We aren't goin' anywhere, mister. Not till we've had a feed. And even then we won't be goin' in the same direction as you.'

'Address me as sir, you insolent oaf!'

Rafferty laughed and just carried on cuttin' up the meat without lookin' up. A whip cracked across Rafferty's back. Rafferty stood up.

The squire got off his horse.

'If he moves, fire. I'm goin to give these two boys the thrashing of their lives. And then you, you Irish swine. You look as though you've eaten herds of somebody's cattle. You'd have been strung up in my day!'

'Whips are for horses, mister. Not boys. Ye've got three

stout men there. Let them give my boys a hidin' and I'll be satisfied. You're astride a hunter. Ye must be a sportin' gentleman.'

'I'm willin', sir,' says the biggest of the three men.

'Yes, me too, sir.'

'And me. I raised that beast myself. It'll be a pleasure, sir.'

'Very well. Go to it. Teach them a lesson they'll never forget.'

The three men set about Harry and Johnny. But the boys very soon put paid to them. The squire was ravin'.

'Run, you swine!' he shouted, raisin' his whip. The boys stood stock still.

'I'll show you what a sportsman I am. Run before my horse or I'll cut you to pieces where you stand!'

The squire lashed Johnny. The blood started from his face. As Rafferty ran towards the squire, one of the keepers shot him in the leg. Rafferty grabbed the squire and hurled him from the saddle. Harry and Johnny took care of the keepers.

'I've never taken a whip to a man in my life,' said Rafferty. 'But I'd whip a dog if I had to. As soon as ye squeal like a stuck pig, I'll be satisfied.' Barely had he raised the whip when the squire screamed like a woman. Two strokes from Rafferty and he was cryin' like a baby.

'That'll do. Harry! Johnny! Get the horses.'

And away the three of them went tracin' the other horse behind them.

A few weeks later they returned to Hartlepool to find Mary Robinson was dyin'. Consumption. After they buried her, Rafferty sold up and they all moved to South Shields. Rafferty had visited it years before and liked the place. It was a town that welcomed fightin' men. It was a tough area. A good place to settle. They bought a lodgin' house in Wellington Street and Annie ran it. She had now grown into a stout, powerful young woman, built more like Harry than Johnny. Not what ye'd call beautiful, but she had a very happy nature.

10

Learning to be Fighters

By the time Harry was nineteeen and Johnny seventeen, Rafferty was fifty-eight. It was 1879. The lodgin' house was a large one and ye had to be an Irish navvy to get in. And damned tough to stay in. Rafferty would pick a good one out and give him a free night's board if he would do a few rounds with Harry or Johnny in the back yard. The more the navvy was able to hand out a thrashin' the better Rafferty liked him. Harry was a very powerful man and when he was sixteen he had been fightin' at twelve stone. In the meantime, Johnny, who was a much lighter lad, had developed into a terrific hitter. Rafferty used to make matches for both of them on Marsden Sands. After they had fought all the best local men he used to send for good men from other parts of the country. Top-drawer men like Toby Wilders of London, Pat Welch of Liverpool, Tom Johnson – another London man – for the highweight championship of England, and Jem Clynds of Bilston. All these men fell to Johnny.

Rafferty was now goin' grey but he was still immensely strong and in some ways rougher than ever. He now drank more than he ever used to. They say he was the biggest man that ever walked in Shields. And to see him standin' in his great, long frockcoat, behind his hackin' black cauldron with a huge iron ladle in his hand, was a sight never to be forgotten. He served broth to hungry kids. His own broth from his own kitchen at the back of his lodgin' house. Over the cloud of scaldin' steam ye'd see his great big face with its deep, hard lines. People seein' him said ye could never imagine Big Peter – which was all he was known by throughout Shields – ever havin' been a boy himself. Nobody could grow into what he was in just one lifetime. He would have to be made just as he was. People were very much afraid of him and would avoid him. But crowds of them would stand watchin' him from a distance. They couldn't take their eyes off him. But with the kids it was altogether different. He'd give the smaller ones little bits of toys that his lodgers had whittled, maybe a cap he'd picked up, or a pair of old boots. But even if he had nowt to give them, he'd always have a gentle word, or a bit of horseplay for the bigger ones. And sometimes he'd whistle them a tune or sing them a funny old Irish song. Although by now Harry was probably the strongest and Johnny the cleverest, Rafferty was still the best.

Woe betide anybody who crossed Rafferty and Sons. They could have handled a mob. All of them supremely strong, tough, and confident. Rafferty had taught both Harry and Johnny how to hunt, how to kill, how to survive. He was the power. And neither of them disputed him. Ever. He was always the boss. Knowin' my father as I do now, I can't imagine his better. But from what he says about Uncle Johnny . . . And what he says about his father – my Grandfather Rafferty . . . Well . . . He was in a world all of his own. A man who could break a bullock's back when he was fifty-eight years' old. It takes me all my time to break a pig's neck. He was once drinkin' in a pub when this big chimney-sweep was lynchin' this skinny, mucky little kid who went up his chimneys for him. He was flayin' this kid with a cane and everybody was just sittin' back watchin' him doin' it, too scared to touch him. Rafferty called him over, and after a few words, with a flick of his wrist he snapped this feller's arm. A jug of beer in his other hand. There was ructions on, but nobody said a word to Big Peter. He sat the kid on his knee, bought him a balloon and carried on drinkin' as if nothin' had happened. When somebody brought a drink across to him he said, 'When I want a drink I'll go and get one. Get out of my sight before I ram it down your gutless throat.'

Both Harry and Johnny were men long before they came of age. Nowadays boys are kids until they are twenty-one. But in my father's day they were men at fourteen. Boys did a man's work for a boy's pay. They soon learnt what ticked. They had to.

Harry was very easy goin' and slow to anger. Everybody says he is today – though not with me. Still, that's for my own good. God only knows what it would be like to have Uncle Johnny or Big Peter Rafferty for a father. I count myself lucky. By the time Harry was nineteen, he had grown into a very big man. He would have been fat if Rafferty had given him the chance. He loved singin' and music, especially to hear his father play the fiddle. When he was about twelve he'd used to enter the Saturday singin' competition at the Variety Hall. One week he won a donkey for singin' 'You can't bamboozle me, you know'. He kept this donkey in a lavvy for three days until his father heard about it. The next week he went back again and won a black pig for singin' 'Sweet Lass of Richmond Hill'. Harry could never look smart in anythin' because he busted out of everythin' he wore. He loved daft jokes. He had the soft side of Rafferty. More so even, I think. Harry, Johnny and Annie all loved fightin', like Rafferty. With my grandfather and my father, although fightin' was a way of life, it was still just a sport. But it was far more than that to Uncle Johnny. Maybe it was because he was the smallest and had to fight that much harder. But whatever the reason, by the time he was seventeen he was one hell of a fighter. Severe, like Rafferty, he was obstinate, aggressive and had a will all of his own. If ye crossed him once, that was it. Ye never got a second chance. He had blue eyes with long lashes like a girl's. Eyes that were soft like his smile one minute, and then frozen hard on his face, the next. Very handsome. Comely. He could have had the pick of the girls. He looked magnificent in anythin'. All the style in the world. As quick with his tongue as he was with his fists. Boy and brute. Determined as hell. He fought to kill. Not just to win. A terrible man to be up against. Even Rafferty would show mercy. He knew when enough was enough. Not Johnny.

In 1882, when Harry was twenty-two, he left home and took to the road with Sarah Cairns of Gallowgate. He had fought all the good men on Tyneside and there wasn't room enough for both him and his brother Johnny in South Shields.

Annie was still runnin' the lodgin' house, and Rafferty was turnin' more to the fiddle and the bottle. The gypsy was in Harry, and he wanted some adventure of his own now. Rafferty just said, 'If ye can't stand on your own two feet now, son, ye never will. Never seek favour and never grant it. Accept one, and you're in debt ten times over. Get on your way. And never forget you're a man.'

The Cairns's were a fightin' family and Sarah was no exception. She was beautiful, not bonny. She had the same hard-soft eyes as Johnny Robinson. And like him, every word she spoke came out like a challenge. Big Peter approved of her. She was tall, fair, tight around the waist and had very long hair even for a woman. Big, swarthy Harry was just the man for her. Tough and strong. Great hands, powerful shoulders, and very popular. First thing they did was to get hold of a Clydesdale and a covered cart. Then Harry built himself a booth that ye could collapse and put up again. One that ye could fight in durin' the day, and sleep in at night. They stuck a few pans and things in, shoved a couple of chickens and piglets in the back. And off they went. Both with cloth caps on, ridin' at the front. Sally's hair flowin' out from under her cap and way down her back. When they stopped, they would tip out the livestock and let them scrat around and get themselves fat. Both Harry and Sarah loved animals though they wouldn't think twice about grabbin' the odd sheep as they passed by. In this way they travelled all over. Harry would be issuin' challenges even before he got his tent up. Sarah would do the singin' and the barkin' for him. Ten bob to go three rounds with Harry Robinson. And six-pence a head for those who only came to watch. Harry also arranged contests and trained fighters himself. Harry and Sarah weren't rich but they more than just got by. After a year's journeyin', little Harry was born – the spittin' image of Uncle Johnny. Still they went on journeyin'. Harry Robinson became well known. And then ... Sally Robinson also. Fine-lookin' woman 'though she was, nobody crossed her. She got tougher and tougher. Harder and harder. My father is the only man who could deal with her. She watched so many fights and learned so much from him, that she could hold

her own in the roughest of company. She had very hard hands
for a woman. And when she made a fist it was like a pickled
prize-fighter's. Gentle, she never was. Good-hearted, she once
was. . . . The life with my father in those early days – the
drinkin', the scroungers, the brutes and the weaklin's – all that
helped make her into the woman she is now.

She knew she had met a good man in Harry Robinson. He
was all that a man should be, and soft-hearted besides. She
had seen him handle the biggest and strongest men that could
be brought forward. And never saw any malice in him. He
was a hard man but a fair man. Sarah Cairns modelled herself
on Harry Robinson. She was proud to call herself Sally
Robinson.

11

Johnny Goes to London

In 1884, when Uncle Johnny was just turned twenty-two, a
competition was held in London to decide the best lightweight
in England. In those days you were either light or heavy, with
nothin' in between. Johnny fought at 10 st. 4 lb. Or over.
Rafferty told Johnny he would have to go and enter for this
competition.

'How will I get to London, father. I've got no money?'

'Walk it, damn ye. It'll do ye good.'

And so Johnny set off on his own for London. When he
got there he went to the place where they were holdin' this
knockout competition. He saw the man in charge and told
him he wanted to enter for it.

'Who, you? Go home, sonny, before you get hurt.'

'I've walked nearly three hundred miles to have a go in
this competition, mister. And that's exactly what I'm goin'
to do.'

'This is for men, sonny. Not farm boys.'

'Look, mister, either ye let me in or I'll knock ye clean off your feet.'

'My word, that's big talk for a boy. Maybe you need a lesson. Come inside. Get into the ring and let's see what you can do.'

The man called across to a bunch of men who were sparrin' in a corner.

'Hey, Sid! Sort this young pup out, will you? He's got too many high-fallutin' ideas.'

Johnny began to take off his shirt but the man stopped him.

'No stripping necessary, sonny. Just get in. We don't want you to catch a cold.'

Sid was about twelve stone and about thirty years old. He looked tough enough but Johnny could see he was carryin' a lot of fat. He tossed Johnny a pair of gloves.

'Here, put these on, lad.'

'No, thanks. I don't use them.'

'Put the buggers on!'

Johnny put the gloves on and got into the ring where Sid was waitin' for him.

'Right, rough him up a bit, Sid.'

Now Uncle Johnny and my father were famous for the tremendous hittin' power they had in both arms. They had both been weaned on navvies who mightn't have known much about the noble art but they were big and they were very hard. Johnny was not only immensely strong, young and highly trained, he had the killer instinct and would take a man to the floor and finish him off there if needs must.

With one blow from his left he smashed Sid's nose and with one blow from his right he laid him out.

'Hmmm,' says the feller in charge. 'You'd better get in and take him,' he told a tall, slim darkie.

'On that showin' he seems good enough to me to go in for the contest,' the darkie said to the feller. 'I don't want to fight the lad.'

Johnny stood in the middle of the ring in full fightin' attitude, his fists held right up.

'Get rid of this heap, here,' he says. 'And you come in with me, mister. I'll show ye if I'm good enough for your contest or not.'

The manager was still very angry with Johnny for what he had said to him at the door.

'I say who goes in for the contest and who doesn't. Now look here, Boston, either you get in there with him and finish him or you can get your arse off the premises and don't come back.'

The poor darkie got into the ring and Johnny made such a mess of him that the manager feller had to put an end to it.

'That's enough. That's enough!!' he shouted. 'You've made your point. What's your name and weight? How old are you and where do you come from?'

When Johnny told him, he gasped. 'What! You've walked all the way from the Tyne? Well, you're keen enough. I'll say that much. Sign these forms and come back on Wednesday night at six o'clock sharp ...

'All right, just put a cross there. Now this is a knockout competition. We divide you up into pairs by drawn lots, and the winners fight it out till there's only two left. Those two will then fight for the lightweight championship of England. If you yield at any time or if you fail to come up to scratch in time, you lose.'

'Fine, that suits me. I'll see ye on Wednesday night,' says Johnny.

On Wednesday night, 16th March, 1884, the hall was packed out. There were prize-fighters and their supporters from all over the country – Birmingham, Glasgow, Bristol, Liverpool. There were big crowds outside who couldn't get in but who were shoutin' and yellin' as though they were at the ringside. Bets were laid inside and out. Right throughout the night while the contests were goin' on somebody was goin' to the door and shoutin' a commentary to the crowd outside. Half of them would be booin' and the other half cheerin' their heads off, dependin' on how their own fighters were doin'.

Johnny's first bout was with Jem Handley and he told his second that no matter what, he hadn't to throw the towel in.

'I'll tell ye when I've had enough,' Johnny said. 'And that

won't be ever. The only way I'm comin' out of this ring before the other feller is if they carry me out.'

Johnny stood five feet eight and a half inches. He wore long breeches tucked into knee socks and leather boots.

'We've got a young lad here who gives his name as Johnny Robinson and I'm told he has walked all the way from South Shields in the far North to deal with the best men the country has to offer. Including our own!'

Johnny had long hair and a very boyish face with a little smile. He waved to the crowd but they just laughed.

'Get ready,' said the referee.

Johnny tied his colours to his corner and pulled off his sark. As he took up his position in the centre of the ring the crowd were amazed. Here was a pleasant boy's head on the magnificent body of a full grown man. Not an ounce of fat and yet no bones to be seen. As he clenched his fists and held out his arms, the muscles swelled and hardened up the length of his arms and right down his back. His skin was perfect. Glowin' pink and without a flaw.

Johnny knocked his man out in five minutes and then walked to the corner and put his sark on. Then he ducked out of the ropes, still smilin'. The crowd were cheerin' like mad when he left the ring. Durin' the course of the night he dealt with all his opponents in the same fashion. First Jem Handley, then Harry Mead and then Arthur Cooper. All fell to his powerful punchin'. At near midnight there were two men left – Uncle Johnny and this other feller whose name is now forgotten for the reason that he refused to get in with Johnny to settle the championship. Johnny was standin' in there smilin' and waitin'. There and then from outside the ring this other feller yielded by offerin' Johnny his hand. Johnny took it and swiftly pulled the man into the ring.

'Now fight. I don't want to win the championship on a default. My father will say I haven't won it properly.'

This feller looked Johnny up and down and turned his back on him. Johnny went up to the MC while he was announcin' the verdict and interrupted him.

'I'm one fight short, mister. If he's scared, give me somebody else. Any weight!'

The MC invited anyone in the crowd to take on Johnny Robinson but nobody stood up.

'All right,' said Johnny to the MC. 'Tell them I'm goin' back to Shields and when I get there I'm goin' to tell everybody that in all London there wasn't a man with enough spunk to stand against me.'

Immediately there was a great disturbance at the back of the hall and a very big man stood up.

'Go on, Jem. Give it to him. Teach the little sod a lesson!'

'I am the undisputed heavyweight champion of London! Either you keep a civil tongue in your head and take back what you've said or I come over there and give you a hiding you'll never forget.'

Johnny, still smilin', waved him on into the ring. Amid terrific cheerin' the heavyweight climbed over the ropes and stripped down. He was well over six feet in height and weighed about fourteen stone. Now my father was between thirteen and fourteen stone at that time and he was very powerful but Johnny and he often fought, and Johnny was the better man. Johnny wasn't bothered in the least about the size of the London champion. Big men fall hard. Johnny had already had three bouts that night but he was still in tip-top condition. He made the big feller look daft by makin' him miss again and again. The big man was angry and the crowd were nearly riotin'. Johnny was able to hit his man wherever and whenever he liked. Head, face, chest, solar plexus – they all got it. In no time the champion was covered in blood. Yet he still fought on gamely. The crowd were now swearin' at Johnny and callin' him everythin'.

'Kill him, Jem! Break his neck! Smash his pretty face in!'

In the middle of all this, Johnny stopped. He held the champion at arm's length and put his arm up to the crowd to quieten them. When they at last shut up enough for Johnny to make himself heard, he spoke to them.

'This is a fair fight and I don't see your man complainin'. He's a good 'un. But I'll tell ye this: the more you shout at me, the harder I'm going to hit him.'

At this, the hall turned into a madhouse. Johnny faced his man again and they both went at it hammer and tong. Johnny, who was brilliant on his feet, just stood still and bashed the champion till he crumpled to the floor. He was in a hell of a mess and that was the end of that.

Strange to say the feelin' in the hall seemed to change. There was nobody in that hall who did not respect Johnny Robinson – the smilin', handsome lad from South Shields. Nobody touched him as he went out but many cheered and wished him luck.

The followin' day the results of the competition were in all the newspapers. Headlines for Johnny. His magnificent physique, his looks, his fierce hittin', and his great skills.

Johnny set off for home next mornin'. When he got back he found himself a hero. He was famous and everybody in South Shields and Newcastle knew of him and he was recognised wherever he went. From then onwards Johnny Robinson never went alone to a fight. He had his own crowds of supporters who would follow him anywhere.

In Uncle Johnny's day it didn't pay to lose. Each side put up an agreed sum and this was paid to a stakeholder – mostly a publican who knew all about the game – at the time the articles were signed. Usually the winner got the lot. Johnny could get £100 or £200-a-side fight now but such big fights were hard to come by and took a lot of argy-bargyin'. So in the meantime he would fight local men for a lot less just to keep in trim.

The mist was still thick one November morning in 1886 when six big men came out of Bolam Woods carryin' ropes and stakes. It was half-past six. In a field next to the wood they quietly and quickly marked out a square and pitched a boxin' ring. After each blow of the mallet – which was muffled with cloths – they would stop and listen for the sound of dogs. By the time the ring was erected fifty people had gathered round. It was to be a secret affair and only those closely connected with the fight had been invited. Ringmen, seconds, referee, stakeholders and chief backers. The principals. Johnny and the bloke he was to fight, Derby Hayes of London, had just stripped when a whistle from one of the scouts warned them that the police were comin'. Everybody ran into the woods chased by police on horseback. All escaped except five spectators. The police also captured the ropes, staves, a sponge, a tin dish and a two-gallon can of fresh water.

On the Monday followin', the match was again arranged but this time it was to take place at Kenton Bar. Seven quick, hard rounds were fought before somebody tipped off the police. Everybody scattered. Johnny was chased right down to the River Tyne where he dived in and swam away. Twice before he had had to do this when fights he was engaged in had been broken up on Newcastle Town Moor. Both times he had safely reached the other side so he wasn't in the least bothered about gettin' his feet wet once more. On the Tuesday night, the police caught Derby Hayes in the Crown and Sceptre and the next day they got Johnny who had come back to arrange another match with Hayes. They were both fined £5 and bound over to keep the peace for six months against sureties of £75 each. All parties concerned decided to call it a draw for the time bein' so nobody got nowt for their troubles.

On the same day that this was reported in the papers, two fellers had been fightin' on Glasgow Green. The police had moved in and one of the men had ran to the Clyde, dived in and was drowned when he was barely a few feet from the far shore. The fight and the chase must have tired him out too much. There were very few places where fights were legal. Especially outside. Not till 1891 in fact. And even then only glove-boxin' was allowed, not prize-fightin' with bare knuckles. Pubs and clubs were the best venues because there were always hidey places. And in any case, they were always protected by the big mobs who were there. The trouble was ye couldn't get ten thousand men into a pub. So big fights had to be outside. Preferably beside a wood or water. Scouts always kept toot every half mile or so. Usually these were on horses and they would come gallopin' up blowin' whistles whenever there was any signs of the Law. Often fighters would be laid up for a long time between matches. This happened with Johnny Robinson because nobody was keen to fight him. Queensberry and his gloves were catchin' on but Johnny always wanted to fight old style with bare fists and cross-buttocks. And always fight to the end. He didn't like decisions on points. Everybody always disagreed with those verdicts. But when a feller chucked the towel in or couldn't come to scratch there was no doubt in anybody's mind.

Many places like the library hall in South Shields would allow boxin' exhibitions even though they wouldn't allow prize-fights. In the eyes of the law, boxin' with gloves was self-defence but prize-fightin' with bare fists was near enough murder. However, more often than not there was little to choose between the two so if you were in the know, money could still be made.

Hundreds went with Johnny when he went to take the Northern Counties Heavyweight Championship from Burke of Wolverhampton.

Thousands went to see him dispose of Jimmy Lowes at Newcastle. And even more, when he finished off Jem Clynds at Bishop Auckland in less than ten minutes. Miners left their pits, traders shut their shops, and ordinary blokes gave up a day's pay. All to see Johnny Robinson fight.

12

Old Wounds

Harry and Sally came back to South Shields in 1887 to spend the Christmas with Big Peter and Johnny; with Annie as well. Ann was a woman, but she was a good one – good-hearted and tough. Travellin' boxin' booths were fallin' more and more out of favour with the law, especially the rough kind that Harry Robinson had. They made up their minds to give up the travellin' and settle in South Shields. Uncle Johnny was famous at the time and very headstrong, and my father wanted to be around to help look after him. He was Uncle Johnny's biggest ally. And his best pal. I think he must have made as much money by bettin' on Johnny as he got from his journeyman boxin' booths. Harry was a great gambler like his father, Rafferty. And he would bet on anythin' – cards, horses, fights, foot racin'. And himself. Uncle Johnny had never been much of a one for gamblin'. He was always too busy with his trainin' and fightin'.

On the 10th March, 1888, when Harry Robinson was twenty-seven he married Sarah Cairns. About this time too Annie married a feller called Gillon. He died shortly, so she married Tom Hardin of Byker and he lasted quite a long time. Rafferty then disappeared. Leavin' everythin' and everybody. And leavin' the lodgin' house to Annie. The big man never came back. They knew he'd got sick of the drinkin' and gamblin' life he was leadin'. His kids were all grown up and his own wife was long gone. The town life was gettin' under his skin. He detested Queensberry and glove boxin'. 'Who the hell wants to pay to see two pansies sparrin' in mittens!' There was far too much talkin' and writin' of letters. Papers to be signed, people to meet who didn't know their arse from their elbow. All interferin' in things they knew nowt about, spoilin' it all.

One time, the squires were the law and they were all for real prize-fightin'. But nowadays, 'The nobles were the last place ye'd look if ye were seekin' nobility. The spineless leadin' the gutless.' Boxers would only fight for a certain price when they should have been grateful for the chance to fight for nowt. So-called champions avoided the best men because they were frightened of losin' their title. 'A man who is scared to defend his rights, forfeits those rights! Ye can't hide a fightin' title under a pillow. Ye wear it round your waist till it's time to drape it over the ropes where the other feller can see it. And take it if he's good enough. It's the greatest honour to be sought out by the best men in the land. Men used to fight every day! Not once a year! No man can call himself a fighter who only comes out like the primroses in spring – when the conditions suit him.'

Rafferty's old wounds were givin' him some bother now. The irons he'd worn thirty years before had been so tight on him that the hair never grew again on his wrists or ankles. No need to brand a man if he's fettered long enough. Whenever he was angry, cold or sweatin', the marks could always be seen as if they'd been painted on him. If his skin was red, the marks showed up white. If his skin went white then the marks turned a dirty purple. He got the 'whites' in the fingers of each hand, and in his toes. As he got older, he'd always be stampin' his feet or rubbin' his hands. The feelin' went. He never ever spoke about it. But ye could tell somethin' was wrong. He became impatient with himself, and the drink didn't help.

All through Rafferty's life, hunger was the order of the day for most people. And dyin' was of no consequence, unless ye were important. So many people just quietly went and died and were never heard of no more. Mind, people were interested in certain kinds of death. Murder and suicide always got attention. The newspapers were full of them. Shipwrecks were another thing. And the more lives lost, the better. Many colliers went down. Not only off the coast and out at sea, but even in the rivers. The Tyne and the Thames as well, in full view. The coal-owners made the hauliers load the boats till they could hardly stay afloat. And when they sank, all they cared about was the tons of coal they had lost. Executions were always news. And when famous hangmen like Marwood turned somebody off, they even told ye how many feet and inches drop he allowed for every poor bugger he hung. He worked it all out with a ruler. There's somethin' the matter with a man who takes a job like that. The soldiers were just as bad. When the starvin' Irish were driven from their homes by the bailiff and his men, if they protested they were charged with bayonets. And if ye were an officer-soldier ye could do no wrong. A carter in Newcastle was sent to gaol under the Mutiny Act for not lendin' his horse and trolley to carry the baggage of a brigade of soldiers who had arrived on the Tyne. And when they had one of their posh balls, half the paper would be taken up with tellin' who danced with who in what dance, in this waltz or that quadrille. Who the hell cares about shite like that? Certainly not Peter Rafferty.

Although human life was made cheap, animal life was just the opposite. Back in 1835 they were supposed to put a stop to baitin', dog-fightin', cock-fightin'. Even man-fightin' wasn't legal in most parts. Yet those were all fair fights. Hundreds of years ago they put a halt on men fightin' big animals hand-to-hand for sport. Lions, tigers, wolves. But in spite of this, it was supposed to be great sport for a dozen men on horse-back to kill animals like foxes and otters with the help of a score of crazy dogs. The difference was that they called these animals vermin, not animals. So, whilst all this was goin' on, ye could get put in gaol for whippin' a horse or kickin' a dog. It was all right to bray a pony to make it drag coal down a mine or to spur a horse to make it win a race, but if ye took a whip to a carthorse in the street, ye had to watch out. This at a time when young kids were always bein' thrashed by the boss for fallin' asleep on the job, mebbes after a twelve-hour shift. One kid of thirteen was put in prison for fourteen days and given eight stripes of the birch on the day he came out, for pinchin' two odd boots from a shoe shop.

My grandfather didn't bother himself much about grown men or women gettin' what they deserved but he hated to see kids ill treated. He thought it was healthy to see kids scrappin' amongst themselves because that would do them good. He said no harm should come to anybody in a fair fist fight. They might get hurt, yes. But that wouldn't do them any lastin' damage and it would put them on their mettle for the next time. He had his own mind about things such as that and my grandmother would never argue with him. Neither on that score or any other. She had been a fine, proud woman herself but she knew her proper place. My father said she was a very gentle woman. Sometimes too gentle – almost soft nearly. She could read and write a bit and she tried to learn me father and Uncle Johnny how to do it. I rather think Uncle Johnny was better at it than my father though. Johnny was very bright and had a memory as sharp as his tongue.

Anyway, God only knows what had happened to my grand-father, Big Peter Rafferty. If my mother or father knew, they never told me and nobody else seemed to know either. I knew that my grandmother Mary had died young. I once saw newspaper cuttin's in a drawer in the lodgin' house about a huge butcher called Rafferty who was bare-fist fightin' in the back end of the eighties in Dublin. So whether he had eventually decided to go back to Ireland and took back his own name or whether this butcher was just a relation of his, I really don't know. I certainly never went to his funeral and never heard any talk of one. Maybe he died in disgrace. You never can tell. My people would clam up about anythin' that had happened in the family. They were the same about Uncle Johnny when his time came.

13

Johnny, the Champion

Uncle Johnny was such a famous figure by 1888 that he often took part in benefits both for himself and for his friends. They were called Grand Assaults-at-Arms and all the best local boxers would be there. Apart from boxin' displays, there would be wrestlin' contests, singin', clog-dancin' and strong-arm acts. All good, round entertainments for the whole family. A professional man like Uncle Johnny who was a full-time prize-fighter and who lived off fightin', needed fights. That was all he knew, all he cared about. If he wasn't actually fightin' he was trainin' for one or talkin' about it. A fighter must always be in perfect shape, but for the two months before a fight he works up to a pitch of superb fightin' condition and this only lasts for a short period of time – the actual peak. He has to get it out of his system. And the only way he can do that is by givin' everythin' he's got to a man as near as makes no matter as good as he is. This is the only way to get rid of all the fire and strength and speed and excitement that's been built up. Labourers can live on spuds and such stuff and can easily get rid of it. But fighters like Uncle Johnny trained for a fight that might last for a hundred rounds. Each contest endin' only by one man not bein' able to stand on his feet, and that might go on for hours. They had to have terrific stamina. Once you get keyed up to such a pitch as that you just have to hit somebody. You're all tensed up because you've taken off weight. You respond quick as a tiger when you're touched or when there's a sudden movement. When a fighter is in that state, keep away. More especially if the fight he wanted hasn't come off.

Whenever Uncle Johnny went fightin', my father Harry was always there. He arranged most of his matches for him and one would stand in for the other at catchweights. Most often they would both be on the same bill. And wherever the two of them went ye could be sure there would be trouble brewin' or a fight in the offin'.

All the fighters used to gather in certain pubs. They were well-known places like the Clayton Arms, the Crown and Sceptre and the Victoria Hotel. They all had painted portraits of Johnny hangin' up.

When Johnny was hard up for a match he would walk into these pubs with his brother Harry and take a look around at all the tough lookin' men, and smilin' he would say to the proprietor, 'I see you've a lot of fine lookin' fightin' men here today, Sammy. I'll fight any man, any weight, for £5 on the grass first thing tomorrow mornin'.' But nobody ever took him up. They all knew him too well. They knew that if they got in the ring with Johnny Robinson they could expect no mercy and that they hadn't a cat's chance in hell of winnin' the fiver.

'Give him his £5, Sammy, and let him go on somewhere else. We hear Anthony Diamond's down the road. Go and seek him. He's more of a match for a man like yourself.'

'Have a drink on the house before you go, Johnny?'

'No, thanks.'

'How about you, Harry?'

'Aye, I'll have a quick one.'

'Right, make it snappy, Harry, and then we'll go and see this Diamond feller. I'll give him diamonds, all right!'

Everybody would laugh and cheer for Johnny. Ye always get blokes like that. Always ready to crawl around when there's a good man about.

My father used to look a lot older than Uncle Johnny. He

was very burly and about sixteen stone with a very stern face like my grandfather. Johnny still had a very boyish face but his hair had got darker now and was very short on top and combed straight forwards. The sides were close cropped. But his cold eyes and tough jaw told you that he was no ordinary boy. My father had a thick, black moustache and jet black straight hair. But Johnny was always very clean-shaven. They both wore thick woollen serge suits specially made by the top-class tailors, Burnard & Son of Newcastle, with gold watch chains and alberts stretched across their waistcoats. Heavy leather boots from Amos Atkinsons costin' 14s 6d a pair. They never wore hats or gloves. Their big, hard, square hands were pickled in brine. My father used to roll along from side to side with very solid steps. But Uncle Johnny was always very straight and light on his feet. He was a good dancer and could do a standin' jump as far backwards as he could for-wards. He could stand in a bar and with his hands in his pockets jump up on to a table or on to the counter just for the hell of it. The glasses would get smashed but nobody would dare say anythin'. They just laughed. The proprietors knew that the Robinson brothers were good for business. Within a few minutes of either of them arrivin' at a pub the place would be packed out with people watchin' everythin' they did and listenin' to all they said.

Although Johnny was the showman of the two, neither of them cared much for these small fry.

In March, 1888 Johnny Robinson and his gang of followers travelled down to London for a fight with Ted Burchell. They were matched to fight under Queensberry Rules at 10 st. 5 lb. with small gloves. Johnny weighed in at ten stone to the very ounce, but Burchell scaled 11 st. 9 lb. Johnny was given the chance to refuse to fight and claim the stakes but he pluckily insisted on goin' ahead with the contest. The referee was Mr Angle who had recently took charge of the fight between John L. Sullivan and Charlie Mitchell in France. The boxin' reporters said that a more perfectly trained man than Johnny Robinson never stood in a ring. That he didn't carry a single ounce of useless flesh. And that he looked fit enough to fight for his life. His muscles stuck out in big lumps when he flexed himself. Johnny was seconded by Barney Shepherd and Coddy Middings, and Burchell by Tom Symonds and Dan McGannon. In the third round Burchell was disqualified for foulin'. Not that it mattered much because Johnny had been all over him.

However, it was a very unsatisfactory end to such an important contest and everybody was disappointed. Particularly Burchell and Johnny. The newspapers said that very high tarrifs had been paid by a select audience at this fashionable saloon in the West End. Good job they were select, because if it had been anywhere else there would have been a riot on. The MC asked if anybody would like to step in to fill the bill. Bill Goode, the 'City Pet', consulted with his advisers, then declined. He was the feller Johnny thrashed after the Lightweight Competition in 1884.

Because travellin' was difficult in those days, the sportin' pages were used to make challenges. Many claimed titles that didn't belong to them and many insults were passed back and forward. On 21st June, 1888 this advert appeared in all the sportin' papers:

I, Dick Burge, will fight Johnny Robinson at 9 st. 12 lbs. for £100-a-side in 10 weeks time. A Match can be made at Mr C. Barrass's Cloth Market, Newcastle. I hope Robinson will come forward and make a Match at once

Signed Dick Burge.

Johnny was quick to answer as he was keen to oblige Burge. Burge was a good fighter under Prize-Ring and Queensberry Rules – glove rules. Although he had been born in Cheltenham he always fought as a Newcastle man where he now lived. The businessmen of Newcastle were always on to Johnny to take up abode in Newcastle or at least to call himself Johnny Robinson of Newcastle. He wouldn't though. It was South Shields or nowt. So the businessmen adopted Dick Burge even though they knew Johnny was the better man. But still they kept on at him.

Johnny sent an answer to Burge that he would deal with him as soon as he had finished with Burchell because a return match with Burchell in Newcastle had already been arranged.

Little more than the Tyne separates Newcastle from South Shields, so on the 20th June, 1888, ferry-load after ferry-load of Johnny's supporters came over to cheer their man. The fight was for £100 at the Percy Street Circus. Burchell weighed in at 11 st. 6 lb., Johnny at 10 st. 2 lb. However, the splendid condition of Johnny and his tremendous hittin' power soon put paid to Burchell. Afterwards, Burchell and Johnny became good pals and Burchell would help to train Johnny or act as his second whenever he got the chance.

When November came, there was tremendous excitement on Tyneside and throughout the country about the forthcomin' match between Johnny Robinson and Dick Burge. Reporters followed them all over and published everythin' that the two of them said or did. Dick Burge's trainin' quarters were at the Royal Hotel in Tynemouth and Jumper Howe was lookin' after him. Johnny, meantime, was trainin' with Ted Burchell at the Victoria Hotel in Newbiggen-by-the-Sea. The fight was to be under Queensberry Rules with five-ouncers – as different from Prize-fightin' Rules as chalk and cheese. However, this way Burge was happy and the contest could be held at St George's Drill Hall, Newcastle. On the day before the fight the final deposit of £50 a side was laid with Mr Graham of the Clayton Arms, makin' a total stake of £200.

Johnny arrived in Newcastle at 10 o'clock in the mornin' of the day of the fight. The official weigh-in wasn't till 2 o'clock in the afternoon but Johnny always got on the scales several hours before he was supposed to just to see how he was doin'. He scaled 9 st. 13 lb. – a pound overweight. He grabbed three sweaters and took off for the town moor. When he got there he ran round it five times. By the time he got back to the Drill Hall he had lost three pounds. That's the kind of man he was.

There was more money invested in this fight than there had been in any contest for years. In the afternoon the Princess and Marquis of Lorne arrived to open the Hall of Physical Science. The newspapers said they should have opened St George's Drill Hall instead – they would have had a far better

reception ... and that very few traders put up their shutters
for the Royals, but all did out of respect for the two boxers.

The contenders had to be in the ring by 8 o'clock on Guy
Fawkes' night, 1888. The seats cost a guinea each and the
gallery was reserved for the Officers of the Four Northumber-
land Volunteers. It was hoped that because of the high prices
only a select audience would be attracted. There was a huge
crowd outside the hall and plenty of fightin' was bein' done
out there as people pushed to be nearest the door. Odds were
even and much money changed hands that neither Burge or
Johnny ever saw. Professor Lowry was the MC, and he said
that to keep the peace with the police the contest would have
to be for only twelve rounds. Not twenty as stated in the
Articles. And if both men were still standin' at the finish, it
would be a draw. Nobody was happy about that. Least of
all, Johnny. Mr Pike of Wolverhampton refereed.

Burge stepped into the 24-foot ring at 9 st. 12 lb., and
Johnny at 9st. 10½ lb.

As Burge climbed in, dressed in his white university-costume,
red socks and leather shoes, there was tremendous cheerin'.
He went and sat in the left-hand corner to wait for Johnny.
Johnny wasn't long in comin'. Johnny had on his breeches,
white socks and canvas shoes. Instead of gettin' straight in
the ring, he defiantly walked right round it with his hand
held up. Four thousand people stood up and went crazy.

Burge was bigger in the arms, shoulders and hips and was
the stockier of the two. But Johnny's slimmer frame looked
as hard as iron. Everybody remarked on his young looks and
his cocky air. He always held his head back a bit, gamely.
Both men were in excellent condition and the spectators stood
up and clapped as they stripped off their jerseys.

Some good skilful boxin' was done and things were about
even up till the ninth round when Johnny's stamina and extra
hittin' power began to tell. By the twelfth round, Burge's
backers were tellin' him to keep out of the way of Johnny's
vicious hands. Johnny now went all out to get Burge who was
a rare dodger and right out of wind. Burge was hangin' on
to Johnny when time was called. Both men standin', the
referee declared a draw and all hell broke loose. Particularly

when Johnny demanded to fight to a finish or at least to go the full twenty rounds. But Professor Lowry made Johnny shake hands as agreed. All the reports said that had the fight gone on Burge wouldn't have lasted the full twenty because of the punishment he was takin'. But, those were the rules and that was that. The general opinion was that Burge was the most skilful and Johnny the hardest. Johnny's backers went crackers at the result but Burge's were more than satisfied to be let off so lightly. Although the backers were nearly all sportsmen to a man, half the fun of it was in the bettin'. Win or lose. In this case of course nobody won nowt. And nobody lost nowt. The selfsame fellers would bet on anythin' from quoits to fives. Even dancin'. Yes, dancin'. There was a miner from Ashington who was always givin' out challenges in the newspapers. Like this:

I, Richard Ferrell, on behalf of my boy do challenge John Turnbull or Robert Brown to dance with clogs at the best 8-toe and best 8-heel-and-toe steps and 8 jig steps for £3-a-side. Each dancer to provide his own music. Apply to this paper for a judge.

On Monday, 24th September, 1889 Johnny fought Jimmy Lowes at St George's Drill Hall for £30. The last time they had met was at the Victoria Running Grounds in 1883. That was the first public open-air fight in Newcastle and Johnny had thrashed Lowes bare-fisted for £3 10s. This time Jimmy Lowes wanted no part of any knuckle and bone and insisted on gloves and Queensberry Rules. It was for the best of ten rounds with two-ounce gloves. Johnny to fight at 10 st. 2 lb. and Lowes at catchweight. Dick Burge seconded Lowes and Ted Burchell acted for Johnny. Lowes thought he had a chance of beatin' Johnny this time although he said Johnny was the best lightweight in the world under the old Prize-Ring Rules. Lowes fought with grit and determination and a hell of a battle there was before the fifth round when Lowes went down again and again. No sooner would he scramble to his feet before Johnny would knock him down again. It couldn't go on. Lowes wouldn't give in so Burge tossed the towel in for him. Some of the old bruisers who were watchin' said it was the bloodiest battle they'd ever seen. Lowes was such a mess that even grown men fainted at the sight of him. From then on Lowes would never entertain Johnny and when he made challenges after that this is what he used to put in the paper:

Wednesday, 27th November, 1889
CHALLENGE
I, James Lowes, of Newcastle hearing tell of so many wanting to box me would like to hear less talk and more business. I will box any man in the North, bar Robinson, from 10 stone to 10 stone 7 lb. with small gloves for £25 per side a fortnight after my match with Lachie Thompson. Man and money ready at any time at The Percy Cottage, Percy Street.

J. LOWES

Lowes was a fighter. Lowes was tough. Lowes was a good sportsman. But Jimmy Lowes was a boxer, Johnny Robinson wasn't. Johnny had all the skills and speed and strength. He didn't mind bein' hit. He thought that a good smack in the mouth or a clout around the ear was just what ye needed to give ye edge. His wasn't the balloon muscle that was all flesh and pulp. He had been hammered into shape by Rafferty. He was solid like cast iron. Hit him and ye hurt yourself. Some said he was an argument against the Ring: that he shouldn't be let loose against a fightin' sportsman. That he fought like a wild beast. That he never knew when to lay off. He hated gloves. Why go to the trouble to pickle your hands in Tom Sayer's brew of turps, whiskey vinegar, horse-radish and saltpetre, if ye were goin' to cover them up? Ye were supposed to use your hands to hurt him, not protect him.

Anybody who stepped into a ring with Johnny Robinson affronted him. It was cheek. It was a challenge. Nobody who stood against him deserved anythin' but a thrashin'. He was the very best. They would have to be taught a lesson. And nobody, bar my father, ever fought Johnny Robinson twice, with bare fists. Gone was the boyish face. Gone was the smile.

The eyes and the hair were now dark. The eyebrows heavy and the jaw set. No more chatter, no more charm. No more style now. Ye paid your respects to him. Ye cheered. Ye waved. Ye said nowt. Ye spoke only when ye were spoken to. And ye always got out of his way. He didn't talk to ye unless ye were a fightin' man. And even then ye had to be good. Very good. When he stepped into the street, ye crossed the road. He wasn't a bully. He only sought out the toughs. But stand against him, disagree with him – and ye got your answer. If ye didn't recognise him, ye were your own fool. He never bruised, he never bled. But, by God, he could draw the crimson from a stone.

Tom Johnson once claimed the Northern bare-fist championship when Johnny was away attendin' to certain business down South. When he came back he immediately demanded a fight with Johnson under Prize-Ring Rules. A match was made at Bishop Auckland attended by bruisers and boxers alike. Johnny's fists cut Johnson's face like knives. He threw him time and again. Cross-buttock. He punished Johnson's body so badly that before twenty rounds had been fought, Johnson was just a bloody shamblin' mess. Still, he fought on gamely until the twenty-ninth when his seconds threw up the sponge sayin' he'd be killed if he went on.

After that Johnny couldn't get anybody to fight him. He offered Alex Roberts, Anthony Diamond, Lachie Thompson, Ted Pritchard – all champions – to fight by Queensberry Rules if that's what they wanted. But nobody was havin' any. Johnny then opened his own boxin' school and used to bill up and comin' fellers as 'Johnny Robinson's Unknown'. Johnny mixed with many sportsmen although he had no carin' for the Turf. One of his mates was a pedestrian called Tommy Burns who for a bet dived off Runcorn Bridge, swam to Liverpool, walked to London, dived off London Bridge and walked back to Runcorn Bridge. All inside nine days. Johnny liked anythin' like that. Time and again he gave out challenges to fight any man in the world between ten stone and 10 st. 8 lb. with no luck.

At last the businessmen of Newcastle persuaded him to come up to Newcastle. That's the only place he would get any good contests. In November, 1889 they set him up in the liquor trade.

Newcastle Daily Leader, 21st November, 1889
Johnny Robinson, of pugilistic fame, has blossomed forth into a Boniface having become the Landlord of The Rose & Crown, City Road, Newcastle. We wish him all success.

That was the start of it all. He should have taken notice of his brother, Harry, and stayed in South Shields. But, ye couldn't tell Johnny Robinson anythin'. Nobody told him what to do. Ever. That pub became the headquarters for the Fancy in the North. Johnny eased up on the trainin' and began to sup with his customers. Ye could drink all day then, and in Johnny Robinson's place ye could drink all night as well. People were always pressin' and persuadin' him to join them. Always wantin' to drink to his health and toast to the great Johnny Robinson, the best man in the world.

In the followin' January, the last attempt to arrange a return match with Dick Burge fell through. Johnny wanted Prize-Ring Rules for a man who could take care of himself with bare fists as well as gloves. But Burge said no. Johnny then said he would settle for a fight to the finish with gloves. But again Burge said no. Johnny carried on drinkin' with his customers. The pub was no credit to him and soon it became the roughest, toughest house in the North. By April, 1890 Johnny was in court over trouble with the Bishop Auckland Board of Health, and shortly after he had to quit the Rose and Crown. When he gave a boxin' exhibition at the Gaiety Theatre in May with Frank Slavin, the Australian champion, the newspapers said he put on a good show but that he was right out of condition.

Harry and Sarah Robinson with young Harry, Johnny, Geordie and
Lily, *c.* 1896

Johnny Robinson, Lightweight
Champion of England, 1884

Johnny Robinson, 1888

14
No Takers

In 1890, the year I was born, my father, Harry Robinson, had his last big public fight. He was to box twelve rounds with Bob Patton, an ex-Guardsman from Manchester, for £20-a-side. Queensberry Rules. It was at the Sunderland Skating Rink. My father knocked Patton down again and again and both sets of supporters tried to put a stop to it to save severe damage bein' done to Patton. But the referee, Jack Ratchford, wasn't an easy man and he let it go on. He felt that Patton should count himself lucky Harry Robinson was usin' gloves. But in the fourth round, when Patton was helplessly crawlin' to his corner on his hands and knees, Mr Ratchford had no choice but to call a halt and declare my father the outright winner.

Meanwhile, Uncle Johnny was still tryin' to get somebody – anybody – to fight him. And wastin' himself at the same time. There was a good up-and-comin' feller in London called Harry Nickless who was makin' a lot of claims for himself. In Scotland Lachie Thompson was doin' the same for his-self. Uncle Johnny's backers tackled them both. Private letters and public letters went backwards and forwards.

Sporting Life, 5th November, 1890
Johnny Robinson of Newcastle writes 'I have now waited many weeks for a response from Harry Nickless to my letter in reply to his challenge offering to box anybody for the 10 st. 4 lb. championship and I think it time that he made a move towards business. I am willing to box Harry Nickless or any other man for the 10 st. 4 lb. championship of the world either a stipulated number of rounds or for endurance

for £200 or £200 a side. The Contest to take place within ten weeks of signing Articles.

Sporting Life, 6th November, 1890
Harry Nickless is surprised at the purport of Johnny Robinson's letter of November 4th wherein he states that he considers it high time that he (Nickless) commence business. Now Nickless would inform Robinson that he is both ready and willing to meet him or any other man in the world. According to his original challenge it was to box anyone in the world at 10 st. 4 lb. If any of the leading clubs would provide a £100 purse, Nickless will stake £50 on the result.

Sporting Life, 8th November, 1890
Johnny Robinson of South Shields, if no purse is forthcoming, would be pleased to box Harry Nickless at 10 st. 4 lb. for £50-a-side.

Robinson would like to hear from Nickless without further pallaver.

Sporting Life, 10th November, 1890
Harry Nickless evidently cannot secure backers for a meeting with Johnny Robinson and he now announces that he will box the South Shields man for the 10 st. 4 lb. championship if any gentleman or recognised club will put up the £100 purse. 'Johnny's' latest is to the effect that he wants no 'pallaver' but will take on the Londoner for £50-a-side. A meeting between these cracks could be well worth seeing.

Sporting Life, 3rd January, 1891
Johnny Robinson is very anxious for a Match just now after a spell of idleness and he writes thus spiritedly to the Sporting Life: 'I observe that Harry Nickless is once more in the field and shall be pleased to meet him for £50-a-side – more if he can get it – at the Ormonde Club, conditions I mentioned in my previous challenge. Seeing that Lachie Thompson is now silent and not showing any signs of trying for the honours he spoke of some time ago, the money that I sent to bind a match with him will do for Nickless to cover.'

Nickless's backers ask Robinson's representatives to meet them at the Ormonde Club to arrange a Match and we hope therefore to see a Match arranged.

Sporting Life, 22nd January, 1891
Johnny Robinson of Shields writes to The Sporting Life: 'Mr Shepherd's kind intervention has prevented unpleasant paper talk between Lachie Thompson and myself. I desire to say no more on the subject than to confirm Mr Shepherd's words – that is, Win or Lose with Nickless I will meet Thompson for £200-a-side. Enclosed a P.O. valued £10 to cover the Scotchman's deposit. Articles based on his original conditions are forwarded to Glasgow.'

In the circumstances we think our Northern champion most polite in this matter.

Lachie Thompson dithered about and wouldn't answer Johnny's challenge until he found that Johnny had finally got matched with Harry Nickless in January, 1891.

When Lachie saw this he then accepted Johnny's challenge. Johnny put it in the papers that he would take on Lachie for £200-a-side straight after he had finished with Nickless. On the 24th January, 1891 the followin' agreement was drawn up between Johnny and Nickless.

ARTICLES OF AGREEMENT

Entered into this Fifteenth day of January 1891, between Harry Nickless of Lambeth, and Johnny Robinson of South Shields WHEREIN they agreed to box under Queensberry Rules at 10 st. 4 lb. for £50 (Open for £100) a side. The Match to be decided at the Ormonde Club, Walworth Road, on Wednesday March 11th, 1891. Ten pound a side is now deposited with The Sporting Life, the remainder of the money is to be posted as follows: £20 a side on February 11th, and the final of £20 a side on February 27th on which date in the event of the men deciding to increase the Stakes to £100-a-side, a further sum of £50 each must be posted. The Sporting Life is to be final Stakeholder and the men to mutually agree to a Referee failing which Sporting Life to appoint Referee. The men to be in the Ring between 8 and 10 p.m. and to weigh at 3 o'clock on the day of Boxing. Gate Money to be equally divided after expenses are paid. In the event of any questions arising which may not be provided for in these Articles the Referee to have full power and authority to decide such question, his decision to be final, conclusive and subject to no appeal in any Court of Law. The Stakeholder shall in any and every case be exonerated from all responsibility upon obeying the direction of the Referee. Either Party failing to comply with any or all of these Articles to forfeit all monies down.

John Robinson
Harry Nickless
              signatures
Witness: W. S. Porter
          E. Shepherd

A couple of days later Ted Pritchard sent a telegram to America to accept Bob Fitzsimmon's challenge for the World Middleweight Championship. In February the Articles were signed between Johnny and Lachie Thompson. He was to fight Nickless on the 11th March and Lachie on the 30th.

By the beginnin' of March, Johnny, who was now bigger than before, was trained to perfection. He was less than ten stone and as the fixed weight was 10 st. 4 lb. he felt he could slacken off a bit. He'd already lost seventeen pounds through trainin' and diet. He was stayin' in Shields and doin' thirty miles a day with swims in the sea thrown in for good measure. He did his indoor workouts at the Harbour Lights. They had a room set aside specially for him where he had a football hangin' from the ceilin' by a rope. Not like the usual punchball with a steadying line underneath. A newspaper man had gone to see him workin' out. He took down a leather ball with him which Mr Murton of Grey Street had specially sewn and blown. It felt to the newspaper feller as though it had been made from Elswick iron. This feller counted Johnny over ten minutes and reckoned he hit that ball 153 times a minute. And Johnny wasn't even blowin' enough to put a little candle out. After the ten minutes the ball was all out of shape and had been hit so hard against the ceilin' that several boards had been knocked out. When the joiner came to repair the damage done he couldn't believe it had been done by one man with one Association football.

But as the time for the fight got nearer, Johnny had started takin' things easier and easier. Before that he had been allowin' himself hardly any beer and only a small glass of gin with his tea. But he now realised this was to be the easiest fight he had ever had. He was way out favourite and he boasted about it. He would kill Nickless for his cheek and then he would murder Lachie Thompson for messin' him about so much. Without botherin' to wash his hands in between. The papers all spoke of his tremendous power and variety of punches. Not only could he strike straight and hard from the shoulder with either hand but he had also mastered the American round-arm which John L. was usin'. On top of this he had a sledgehammer corkscrew uppercut. Again with each hand.

When Uncle Johnny and my father arrived at Kings Cross there was a trainload with them. They were met by umpteen people. Fleet Street was like the Bigg Market, there was so many Geordies there all drinkin' and cheerin' for Johnny Robinson. They all celebrated at Tiny Hawkins' establishment, the Surprise, in Farringdon Street. Johnny as well. Johnny's party was really confident. On the way to the weigh-in next day they stopped by the *Sporting Life* office to put down a further deposit against the fight with Lachie Thompson. The top fighters of the day were all there to see Johnny Robinson gut and fillet Harry Nickless. Lachie Thompson and his mob were there as well. Bets were laid six to four on Johnny beatin' both Nickless and Thompson.

By the time Johnny arrived with his gang at the Ormonde Club, he was full of whisky. He could afford to drink what he liked and still beat Nickless. With his eyes closed. When Nickless climbed into the ring at ten past ten on the night of 11th March, 1891 he looked very powerful and was in tip-top shape. When Johnny got in he looked good but his supporters explained that he was a bit slower because he had a 'cold'. The first two rounds were brisk with plenty of good punchin'.

Johnny was well ahead at the end of the fifth round due to his hard hittin'. But he wasn't quite so quick on his feet as Nickless. In the sixth round, Johnny, the great stayer, was unsteady and slow. Nickless put in a right to Johnny's jaw and as Johnny tried to side-step, he slipped against the post and broke his ankle. He turned to Mr Percy who was his main backer and said, 'Jim, my leg's gone'. Charlie Mitchell was standin' next to Mr Percy and he told him to throw in the sponge.

'No. Let him carry on,' said Mr Percy. He had too much staked on Johnny to give in. Johnny got up only to be knocked down six times in a row. He couldn't stand up properly and Nickless could do what he liked with him now. Johnny was hangin' on to the ropes with one hand, on his knees, and punchin' at Nickless with the other. Nickless tore into him as he knelt there takin' whatever Nickless gave him. Nickless was bendin' over him and bashin' his head against the corner post with both fists, never lettin' up for a moment. This was the first time Johnny Robinson had ever been down and Nickless wanted full honours for puttin' him there. He'd got him right where he wanted him now. He slashed at Johnny again and again. The great Johnny Robinson was beat. He was a pitiful sight, and couldn't cope any more. The referee stopped the fight and spoke to Johnny who was hangin' on to the ropes to support his legs. Johnny held out his hand as a token of defeat and the referee declared Harry Nickless the winner. The doctor put Johnny's leg in a rough kind of splint and they carted him off to St Thomas's Hospital. He was told he'd have to stay there for six weeks to get it put right.

Straightaway Johnny fell from favour and only his best friends stood by him. The papers criticised his fightin' sayin' that he hadn't used his height and quick legs to their proper advantage. . . . His feet were too far apart. . . . All his old wickedness had gone. . . . He didn't show his natural cockiness and dash. . . . His punches weren't fierce enough. . . . He was slow. . . . He was unsteady. . . . He had let everybody down. . . . Thousands of pounds had been lost on him. . . . Johnny was left in the hospital while Harry and all the rest of his supporters went back to Newcastle and Shields. His backers forfeited the £100 laid against Lachie Thompson but Lachie gallantly sent back £50 as a solatium for Johnny. He showed himself a good sport, him. Tiny Hawkins visited Johnny several times when he was in hospital and put adverts in the papers sayin' that he'd had many letters from the North askin' about Johnny's condition. And that he was in good spirits and was makin' a steady progress. On the 1st April, 1891 Johnny left the hospital on crutches and Tiny Hawkins put it in the paper that Johnny would be pleased to see any of his friends at the Surprise before he left London to return home.

When he came back he was wearin' a paris-plaster and had chucked away his crutches. Somebody had got him a big cane walkin' stick instead. Probably it was Tiny.

A benefit was planned for Johnny at the Gaiety Theatre in Newcastle for three weeks' time. But it didn't come off. He had done himself good and proper. And now he was finished. For good.

From time to time he did the odd exhibition and had a few local scraps. His School-of-Arms in Clayton Street no longer attracted the people it used to. Johnny Robinson's fightin' career had ended. But that wasn't all – not by a long chalk. He couldn't have ever dreamed of the things that were goin' to happen to him yet.

There was never any talk in the house about what became of Uncle Johnny after the Nickless fight. And the fight itself was never mentioned either. But I learned a lot from other people who knew Uncle Johnny. Will Curley the promoter, Tom Murphy, Harry McDermott. And some of his old followers. I've never been a talker myself and wouldn't dare repeat what I'd heard to my father. When I was a kid I'd once asked him if it was true that Uncle Johnny had turned to drink and he clouted my ear so hard I was deaf for three days. Anyway, turn to drink, he had done. All the money he had left from his winnin's went on drink. First beer. Then gin. And then the whisky. For a few years after his fight with Nickless he earned a bit from exhibitions and teachin'. But then he got so bad his exhibitions became a farce with him drunk and hopelessly out of condition. He wasn't even a shadow of his former self. Nobody would come to his boxin' classes any more. He either wouldn't be there at all or he'd be late. And if he was there he'd be drunk and swearin' and rude to the people who came to him. Nobody wanted anythin' to do with him except a few friends like Foreman Tye, the world champion cyclist. These fellers were still at their prime then, as Johnny should have been. He'd had a marvellous reputation and had put it all in a bottle. Dick Burge and Jimmy Lowes, Jem Carney and Harry Nickless, Ted Pritchard and the others all had big things yet to come. But still Johnny was able to find money for drink from somewhere. From his brother, Harry, from his friends and from any of the big businessmen who might still have some respect for him. Anyway he was able to get enough drink to reduce him from one of the world's best – a man always noted for his tremendous strength and stamina – to a sick old man in five years. One of his greatest admirers told me he'd seen Johnny lookin' just like a sloppy ghost. With a constitution like his he must have had to swallow gallons and gallons of hard liquor to get like he was in 1897. He had a picture taken of himself when he was about thirty-three years old. What a pathetic sight. No muscles on his arms. And they were stuck up like two sticks. Saggin', useless thin fat on his body. Navvy's trousers tied with string. And broken boots with no laces in. Soft hands. There he was standin' in a fightin' position without an ounce of fight in him. He must have scraped a few shillin's together so he could have a picture of himself to show his pals. He used to take it round the pubs and show anybody who'd listen to him that that was a picture of him, the great Johnny Robinson. He must have been shameless to do a thing like that. Although there was nothin' left of him, he was still game. His reputation was enough.

Like once he was drinkin' in the Marsden Inn with Foreman Tye. They were sittin' havin' a pint of beer and Johnny had this great big walkin' stick of his leanin' against one of the chairs. There were a bunch of miners at the next table who'd had too much to drink. They were keep makin' jokes about Johnny's stick. When Johnny got up to go for a pee he left his stick deliberately and hobbled off to the lav. They started laughin' at him. Without stoppin' or even turnin' round he

Presentation for Johnny
Robinson (*bottom right*), *c.* 1892

Fallen idol, Johnny Robinson,
1896

BOB FITZGERALD   BILLY GALLEY   STOKER ALLAN   JONNY ROBINSON
10 st 7   9 st 6   8 st 10   8 st 10

Young Johnny Robinson with
the Fancy, 1913

Young Johnny, Featherweight
Champion of the North, 1913

says, 'I'll see you lot when I get back.' One of the miners says to Mr Tye, 'Who the hell does he think he is?' 'That's Johnny Robinson,' says Foreman Tye. At that they all scarpered and by the time Uncle Johnny got back their table was empty.

Some said he would bully people into buyin' him a drink. And that he was a womaniser. I can certainly believe that because he was a very handsome, strong-lookin' man when he was younger. And very vital. Whether in his breeches and pink muscles in a ring or in the street in his serge suit and chain, he was a very strikin' man. And everybody turned their heads when he walked past. He'd had no time for the women when he was in his prime but after the Nickless business he had plenty of time and money for the women and they would flock round him. First the women of fashion. And then the whores. But after a while only the lowest of their kind would bother with him. At first he had lived at a hotel in Newcastle, then at his brother's, and then at his sister Annie's who was married to Tom Hardin of Byker. Then in lodgin' houses. And all the time gettin' worse and worse till in the end he had nowhere to go. Nobody would have him. He had no money to stay anywhere and no money for drink. He did a few light labourin' jobs which was all that he was up to. But as soon as he got paid he got drunk. And if he got a sub he'd drink it and not go back. He got the sack so many times that nobody would take him on.

He'd have drunk piss if it had fermented. His skin was like glass, and stained with patches of bile. His body went, then his pride, and then his brain. He looked dazed and he would always be whisperin' silly things to himself. Havin' daft dreams that scared him. God made him to be champion of the world, and by the time he was thirty-five, he was nowt but a dirty, drunken tramp.

At five past seven at night, on the 23rd November, 1897, Johnny Robinson knocked on the door of the South Shields Union Workhouse.

E

15

Workhouse

Uncle Johnny must have been really desperate to go into that place. It was more degradin' than goin' to jail. The gate porter admitted him and entered him up in the Porter's Rough Admissions & Discharge Book as:

Robinson, John. Age 35. Labourer. C. of E. Address: Thrift Street. Relations: None.

Even though Uncle Johnny was in an awful state he still managed to scrape up enough pride not to let on that he had a brother and sister living in town. He knew he would shame them if they found out. He'd pestered them enough already for drink-money. The address he gave was of the Thrift Street lodgin' house where he had been stayin' until he got kicked out.

People say that in some workhouses they give poisoned bread to tramps because nobody outside would ever know or care. Whether it is the truth or not, who knows. But everybody knows that many go into the House on their feet and come out on their backs. Johnny certainly couldn't have had much pride left to sink so low as that. They took him to see the Master and he was told to read the rules. He couldn't. So the Master read them out to him in no uncertain manner. Johnny Robinson was a pug so he was able-bodied and would have to work in the quarries. If he didn't work he'd get kicked out. And if he gave any trouble they'd put him straight in jail. No bail. No court case. No palaver. They'd just send for the police and have him put away. Either there or the loony bin. And once they get you in the Bin, ye never come out. Johnny was taken away for the delousin' treatment. Everybody got that, be ye clean or be ye dirty. This was done in a shed in the yard which had cold water comin' down from a tap in the ceilin'. There were three old blokes standin' naked in this shower. Two were scrubbin' each other down with this green stuff from a bucket. The other one was tryin' to cover his privates because this big nurse was watchin'. Johnny was told to get stripped and get in.

'I'm not dirty,' he says.

'Get in!'

'I'm not stayin'. I want to get out of this place.'

'You're too late. The doors are bolted. Now get in there! This minute! Or else I'll box your ears for you. We know just how to handle the likes of you!'

'Wait till those fellers come out.'

'Now! In there with them! You can all pig in together. You're no different from anybody else here.'

'I'm keepin' my drawers on then.'

'There's no underclothes worn in this establishment. Nobody wears them. Man or woman, Which are you?'

The big nurse shoved Johnny into the shower with all his clothes on and Johnny fell to the ground, knockin' the bucket over. It splashed on to the side of his face and got in his hair. It burned him and his face turned red and raw wherever the stuff had splashed on him. There he was. Spent. Lyin' down. Pushed on his back by a toothless git who shouldn't have been fit to lick his boots. And he couldn't even get up. One of the old fellers helped him up. They all shared the same soakin' towel. The nurse then cropped his hair with a pair of big scissors with all kinds of greasy hair stuck to them. She made his head all spikey and tufty. She then took a cut-throat, without soap or water, and fetched it up to his crown right around. Little trickles of blood ran down his neck as he struggled to get free from the porter who was holdin' him down. They then threw a grey jacket and trousers on the floor and told him to put them on. Johnny was swearin' at them the whole time but he could do nowt about it. Not a bloody thing. He'd made his own bed and now he was havin' to lie in it. He'd really let the side down. And the whole family. The trousers had a big 'P' stamped on the backside and the legs. This was

to let everybody know that he was a pauper when he went
out to work in the gravel pits or wherever. When he'd put
his clothes on he asked for somethin' to eat.

'It's bedtime for you, my lad. You'll have to wait till tomorrow. Don't worry, we'll have you up early enough. This
is the workhouse. You'll get no lie-ins here.'

Johnny was taken away to the men's dormitory. There were
two men to each bed and scarcely any room between any of
the beds. They pointed to a bed with a young feller in it who
was coughin' his guts up.

'Get in.'

The young feller was awake. He smiled at Johnny.

'Just come in, mister? Had nowt to eat? Here's some crusts
I've saved up under me piller. I can't eat them. I've got
consumption. At leasts that's what the other blokes say.' So
Johnny ate up the poor bugger's crusts.

Next mornin', after gettin' washed right under the eyes
of the nurse and the porter, they were all led to the dinin'
hall. A huge room with a very high ceilin' and windows way
up – well out of reach. The tables and benches were all bare
scrubbed wood. Breakfast was 7 o'clock. Stone basins with
what was supposed to be gruel in them were given to each
inmate as he trooped past the cook's counter. Warm water
with oatmeal floatin' on top. After ye'd drank that they poured
cold tea into it and gave ye a thick crust of bread. After that
ye washed your own basin in cold water and handed it in.
At 8 o'clock the women were divided up into lots. Those who
had to clean and scrub the tables, walls and floors. Those who
had to do the laundry. Those who had to sew up torn clothes
and sheets and that. And those who did oakum pickin'.

The men were split up into two lots. Those that worked
outside. And those that stayed in. The ones that stayed in
chopped wood or ground meal. Grindin' was one of the worst
jobs ye could get – because ye had to walk round and round
all day and every day turnin' this big iron crank until ye
dropped. Every man had a quota to do and if he didn't do it
ye all got punished. So ye couldn't carry anybody who was
weak or lazy. Punishment was either jail, not bein' allowed
out for a month, bein' locked up on your own, your baccy

taken off ye, or your tea and vegetables stopped. What little meat ye got ye wouldn't have missed anyway.

Johnny was taken out to a quarry in Jarrow in a gang. And everybody they passed in the street knew just what they were. Johnny's job was to smash granite and whinstone and other hard rocks that had been brought in 'specially. He had to break them up into gravel with a mallet or a sledgehammer. These gravel pits or stone-breakin' yards were always in public places so that if any passerbys saw the paupers loungin' about they could report them. People were encouraged to do this because they were told it would save them money in the long run. If there was a shortage of stones, the paupers had to dig holes in the ground and then fill them in again with the earth they had just dug up. This was to keep them from bein' idle or from gettin' up to any mischief.

At 6 o'clock they knocked off and went back to the House. They walked there and back and sometimes to a lot farther than Jarrow or Hepburn. When they got back to the gates Johnny could hear a kid yellin' his head off.

'What's that all about?'

'It'll be some kid they've caught runnin' away. They always give them a good hidin'.'

'What with, for Christ's sake? To make it scream like that?'

'The whip or the birch. The one cuts, the other bruises. So there's little to choose between the two.'

'What about the kid's parents?'

'He probably hasn't got any. None that'll own him, anyway. But even if they were here there's nowt they could do to stop them. They all get separated – the man from his wife and the mother from her bairns. You even get punished if you're caught talkin' to your own wife, here. See, what they do is this. The girls are learnt to be servants so they won't become whores. And the boys are learnt to be shoemakers or soldiers. Them jobs don't need no capital. Anyway, any kid brought up in a place like this would be glad to get into the Army. They're just the sort they want. Full of hate, and dead tough.'

On the Sunday, Johnny wouldn't go to the Workhouse Chapel because he said he was a Catholic. And they wouldn't let Catholics out on their own to go to a church in town because they said they always got drunk. So it was the Protestant Chapel or nowt.

On the Monday, Johnny was set on bone crushin' in a hut near the workhouse. It stank. It had rained the night before and the gravel pit had got flooded. So they couldn't go there today. One of the fellers said to Johnny, 'Ye hear them moanin' about turnin' a lousy fuckin' capstan handle in the lousy fuckin' mill. But that's nowt compared wi' this. You're always gettin' these filthy bone splinters stuck in ye. And they fester before the fuckin' mornin'. And some of the poor bastards here are so fuckin' hungry ye'll see them scrapin' the lousy fuckin' marrer out of the rotten fuckin' bones and eatin' it. Filthy fuckin' stuff it is an' all.'

The next day Johnny was sent out to the granary. He got away and went into Shields' market. He met some of his old mates in the pubs round there and got drunk. When he went back to the workhouse they locked him away. Mopin' idiots, ravin' madmen and drunks were all treated alike. Shut up in a room with barred windows. And dry bread chucked at them. Some were chained up.

A couple of days later the workhouse doctor came to see Uncle Johnny and got him out. This doctor was a canny feller and tried to do his best for the paupers. But he had no powers. The Master was the boss and the Board of Guardians were in charge of him. If the nurse or Master didn't like what the doctor prescribed then they just didn't give it. Like in Johnny's case the doctor said he was a maniac-drunkard or somethin' like that. Not that he was crazy but that the drink had pickled his brain and that he couldn't help himself. He said Uncle Johnny should be allowed a gill of beer a day. But that was out. They had even banned beer at Christmas because some of the staff had got drunk one year. That was the Guardians' doin'. They were a law to themselves. Most of them were ordinary blokes in business. They had to have so much a year income before they were appointed. Not because they gave anythin' out of their own pockets. But because money was a sign of good breedin'. They used to meet every now and again to study all the books. And there was books for all sorts of things in the workhouse. They would act like judges sayin' what had to be done and what hadn't been done. What punishment this or that pauper should get. They would sit there havin' great slap-up feeds with wine – the lot – while the paupers were locked inside eatin' oatmeal in water and drinkin' cold tea.

The Master was usually an old army sergeant or such like. The nurses were treated as worse than the lowest scrubber in a hospital. It was hard to get decent people to work in a workhouse. So the Guardians had to hang on to what they'd got. When things got too bad – say a Master was reported for fiddlin' with the young girls – then he'd be given a toppin' testimonial and packed off to a workhouse somewhere else where he wouldn't be known.

Kids without parents were called 'deserted bastards'. That's what the Guardians used to write down in the book. The way I was brought up, that was the worst of all the bad words. That was somethin' that ye shouldn't even call your worst enemy by. The Guardians used to get paid hire for gettin' the inmates to do labour for a friend of theirs. If one of them was a grocer or greengrocer he used to sell his stuff to the workhouse at special prices. Although they might talk and write in a high-falutin' way, most of them were as mean as sin.

When a pauper died the workhouse kept every mortal thing he had. Once when a feller with a wooden leg died, they took it off. His wife begged them to put it back before they buried him so that he'd look right. But would they hell. They kept sayin' it belonged to the parish.

There was nothin' to do in the workhouse except work, sleep and eat. There was no furniture to speak of. A few hard chairs and stone steps were all there was to sit on. There was no music allowed or cards or anythin' like that. No entertainments. And if ye could read ye read the Bible. In the workhouse they gave ye just enough to stay alive till ye died.

My Aunt Annie told me so much about all this. About Uncle Johnny in the workhouse. But most of it was told to me by a Catholic priest – I cannot speak his name for fear of doin' him hurt – who used to visit the place. He'd been a

Guardian himself at one time before he gave it up because he couldn't stand it no more. He said they were a bunch of hypocrites. I used to talk to this Father quite a lot at one time – when I was about fourteen – because he wanted me to go in for the Church. I hadn't much time for Uncle Johnny for lettin' himself go like he did, and the Father would get angry at me and tell me that I had no feelin's, and that I would never be any use to the Church if I carried on thinkin' that way. The Father had spoken to Uncle Johnny when he was inside and had got it out of him what had happened. But I still think it was a shameful business all the same. Even a sewer-rat has some pride. At least it can fend for itself. Which is more than ye could say for Johnny Robinson.

My father eventually heard that Uncle Johnny was in the workhouse and he brought him out. He knew that Uncle Johnny was in a bad way but he never knew that things were as bad as this. He gave Uncle Johnny enough money to get by on and he went to live in a lodgin' house. But his drinkin' got worse and worse and he was put out of one lodgin' house after another. In May, 1898 he went to live in Bauld Fox's lodgin' house in Barrington Street. On Friday, 10th June Johnny couldn't get out of his bed in the mornin' so Mr Fox sent for the outdoor relievin' officer from the workhouse to do somethin' about him. When he came, Johnny was lyin' on the floor with blood comin' out of his nose and ears. He sent for the doctor. He came at 8 o'clock at night and gave a note to Mr Fox to have Johnny taken away. But when they came back for him at 10 o'clock he was already dead. He was thirty-six. My father hadn't seen him for two months. And he'd died without a priest. At the inquest Mr Fox stated that Uncle Johnny had been at his place for a month and durin' that time had eaten next to nowt and that he had been drunk every single night. The coroner said Johnny had died of apoplexy due to severe drinkin' habits.

Again, now that he was dead Johnny Robinson was headlines in all the papers. Everybody talked about how great he had once been. The *Mirror of Life* said:

Death of Johnny Robinson

Were we asked to name a fighter in these days of modern boxing more nearly approximating to Hickman, the terrible gas-man, than anyone else we have met, we should unhesitatingly say Johnny Robinson of South Shields . . . Johnny died suddenly on Friday night from an affection of the heart. . .

The local newspapers proudly said that he was the best fighter the North had ever seen. Even the London papers admitted he was the 10 st. 6 lb. champion of the world under Prize-Ring Rules. And lots of things like that.

His funeral was a tremendous do and all the fighters includin' his old opponents came. Everybody connected with the Fancy and other sports were there. People came from London and all over and all kinds of speeches were made.

Sporting Man, 15th June, 1898
Funeral of Johnny Robinson

Yesterday afternoon the remains of the late Johnny Robinson of South Shields who died on Friday night last, the once famous 10-stone champion of England were interred at the beautiful cemetery at Harton amid many tokens of deep sorrow. The cortege left the residence of his brother Harry Robinson, Mill St., South Shields, shortly after three o'clock and proceeded to the cemetery by way of King St. and Westoe Lane followed by a large number of well-known boxing men and many of the public. On arrival at the cemetery the procession was met by the Rev. Father Drakes S.J. who, after a short service in the Church, conducted an impressive ceremony at the graveside. The chief mourners were Harry Robinson, brother, Annie Hardin, sister. Thomas Hardin, brother-in-law, John Cairns, Mrs Wealands and Master Wealands. The coffin which was of pitch pine with brass mountings was suitably inscribed. There were many floral tributes in token of the esteem in which Johnny, perhaps the most famous of all local pugilists, was held.

God rest his soul. . . . He must surely have made his peace by now. And I'm truly sorry for the awful things I've said about him.

16

Robinson's Lodging Houses

I was eight years old when Johnny Robinson died. I didn't much understand what was goin' on apart from my Uncle Johnny dyin' and gettin' buried. I didn't go to the funeral but our Harry did. He was a lot older than me then. My father and mother would always chase me out whenever they were talkin' about Uncle Johnny and all that. Or when important people came to the house. But I still heard a few things. I remember my father bein' very angry and talkin' about a doctor-professor who had been given the right to let his students cut up the bodies of those who died in the workhouse. This professor said that if they had no relatives to claim their bodies, they became the property of the corporation by rights. And that nobody should object so long as their remains got a Christian burial in the college grounds. That was after him and his students had done with them.

Harry would tell me quite a lot because he's always been a great talker. He'd tell ye any secret ye wanted to know. And he'd read stuff out of the newspaper for me when I was too young to do it for myself. Harry said it was a disgrace that there was more in the newspapers about Mr Gladstone dyin' than there was even about our Uncle Johnny. And him a champion of the old Prize-Ring. The newspapers didn't like boxin' either. It was fine and dandy for a British soldier to shove a rusty bayonet into the belly of a Boër farmer with his legs blown off. But it was brutal and immoral for two evenly matched British athletes to have a set-to. Even though they both wanted nothin' better. They'd give the news and results of cricket, quoits, bowls, aquatics. Fives, hare coursin', pigeon-flyin' and billiards. Even chess. But never boxin'. A vicar, who happened to be very rich heself, said that illness was as much a sin as idleness and that what the country really needed was a good old-fashioned snowstorm to put paid to the paupers and beggars. No wonder there was so many people puttin' ropes round their necks. Many went to Canada, to the mountains of the Klondyke, because there was a big gold-rush on. But there was always somebody prattlin' and preachin' about what would happen to ye if ye left dear old England. They said a person must have no morals to go and seek gold. And that there would be all sorts of evils like drinkin' and gamblin' and bad women over there. I wonder what they thought they had here. It seems to me that it makes no matter whether ye do it here or there, if that's the way you're made. Again, a lot of men joined up to go and fight in the Boër war. But they couldn't have liked it much when they got there, because accordin' to the newspapers, for every ten that stayed, one deserted. And that's an awful lot if ye add them all up. A draper in town went bankrupt and was fetched up. The judge asked him why he hadn't paid his debts and the draper said he couldn't pay his if his customers didn't pay theirs. And that he had the War to thank for that.

'What's the War got to do with it?' asks the judge.

'Most of my customers are the wives of soldiers,' replies the draper.

'Well make them pay just the same,' says the judge.

'What, by sendin' the soldiers summonses along with their rations?'

'If needs be, yes,' says the judge. 'You're not excused.'

So much for newspapers. And the rest of the world.

By 1899 there was five of us kids. Harry, me, Geordie, Lily, and little Mary Ellen. My father was then thirty-nine and had given up goin' away to fight. He was now too busy with his lodgin' houses. In any case, at eighteen stone there wasn't many fellers around that were bigger than he was, and very few that would take him on with bare fists. Because, like my Uncle Johnny, my father loved the old Prize-Ring Rules – the way he was brought up. Not that he still didn't do the odd bit of 'business' when it came his way.

Big as he was, there was very little fat on him. And the old-style fighters carried on for a long time: Jem Mace was sixty when he fought a good man like Dick Burge in his prime.

My father and mother were always buyin' up lodgin' houses or properties to be used for lodgin' houses. They had places in Long Row, St Hilda's Lane and Mill Street. The Mill Street one, No. 22, where I was born, used to be a police station. The cells were converted with beds for the lodgers. My mother still looks after that one. It's a huge place. And all the big family do's have always took place there.

Lodgers are made up of all kinds of people. But they are all rough. What can ye expect for a penny or tuppence a night? Some are pretty tough as well but that doesn't bother my father or mother in the slightest. I think my mother is always harder in her dealin's with them than my father ever is. My mother is a very big and very strong woman and nothin' shocks her. But she won't have ye take the Name of the Lord in vain. She looks after the Mill Street lodgin's by herself. I've seen her knock more men down than my father. Women, she just takes by the scruff of the neck and tosses them down the stairs. They are no trouble at all to her. Ever since I was a kid I can remember seein' women fightin' in the lodgin' houses and in the street. It's just the same now. Usually it's because one of them has pinched somethin' belongin' to the other one. Or over a man. They take their blouses off and fight like men with their fists up. In their petticoats. My mother will stand and laugh at them and enjoy it as long as it isn't inside her lodgin' house. Otherwise she'll sharp put them out and they wouldn't get back in for love nor money. She enjoys a good fight as much as any man I've ever met.

My father's Model lodgin' house has a lot of seamen in it. Probably because it's right on the riverside. But in our Harry's place in Barrington Street there's a lot of tinkers stay there. They make bait-cans, wire baskets and toastin' forks. Anythin' that can be soldered over a fire. And they'll mend anythin' ye can give them. They would stop a sieve leakin' if ye paid them to. Their women make velvet pincushions and tea-cosies. Clippy mats and anythin' like that that can be made from bits of rags. Then they go and sell them in the market to earn their keep. Others'll stand a few yards down the street from the lodgin' house and sing away to get a halfpenny or a penny for their board. There was some clever coopers as well when I was a kid. I can think of one feller who would come in with a whole lot of scrap-wood and wire and stuff and in half a day he'd turn out a barrel fit for the best port wine. Quacks. Every lodgin' house has its quacks. A lodgin' house without a quack would be like a church without a priest. As long as they pay their board they can go and poison who the hell they like. Anybody daft enough to swallow their sulphur balls or drink their dirty-lookin' tar tonics deserves all they get.

No other woman would dare to go around like my mother does. With a great thick sackcloth apron and two huge baggy pockets at the front full of money. Her takin's. Ye hardly ever see her without it on. If anybody didn't know her and came to beg a penny she'd fetch them such a clout around the ear they'd never do it again. My father's dead soft, though, when it comes to his lodgers. He'll let them off without payin' and all sorts if he thinks they're too poor to pay. It's amazin' how many come back to him – even after a long, long time – to pay him back. But ye'd never catch me mother doin' owt like that. Ever since I can remember she's had a great big black pot of thick soup always on the fire. She'll eat one of those every day of her life. Apart from her meals. Every now and then she'll just go and stir it up and help herself to a few ladlefuls. Straight out of the pot on the fire. No spoons, no plates. No nowt. Just standin' there suppin' it. My father has a little shop downstreet from his Model lodgin' house, called the Green Shutters. And he sells second-hand clothes to the lodgers and anybody else that has a mind to buy his rags. He keeps horses as well. On the Lawe Top. When we were lads we used to help to look after them. He hires them out to carters, French onion-men and people like that. My mother looks after the pigs and chickens as well as her lodgin' houses. And my sister still helps with them. Once a week one of the girls takes a horse and cart from my father's and shovels all

the horse manure on to it. Then they go down to my mother's
and get a load of the pigs' stuff. Then they cart it away to
a farm and sell the lot. My mother'll reach into the sack-pocket
in her apron and pull out a halfpenny for anybody – drunk,
woman or kid who'll bring her a pennorth of peelin's for the
pigs. She's a hard business woman. Borrow a tanner, and it'll
cost ye sixpence-halfpenny to pay it back. Borrow a bob and
it'll cost ye one-and-a-penny. More than that, ye won't get –
come Hell or High Water. She's always been the same.

As soon as we were old enough we were all sent to school.
My father said learnin' was important. And it doesn't say
that just because you're a fighter ye have to be a fool. He
said if ye had hard fists and an educated mind ye could go
anywhere. Do anythin'. Hold yer own with anybody. Mind,
my mother mightn't have been a scholar, but she could tot
up anythin'. Either on her fingers. Or, if they weren't sufficient,
on her rosary beads.

To show how serious my father was, I remember him tellin'
me about how, when I was just a few months old, he had
jumped on to a railway track in front of a train to grab hold
of a little girl. After the train had gone by, he fetched this
kid across the line and lifted her back up on to the platform.
The father was standin' waitin' in tears. He made a hell of
a fuss and said if there was anythin' in the world he could
do for my father, he would do it. My father said to him,
'Who are ye?' The feller told him his name and that he was
a schoolmaster. 'Right,' said my father. 'Ye can learn is to
read and write. I'm sick of makin' crosses.' He did as well.
A bit. He became canny good at it. Better than me mother
any rate.

My mother agreed with my father on this score of books
and learnin'. Not that she ever disagreed with him anyway –
tough though she was. She's always said any fool can make
a cross, but it takes an educated man to know for sure what
he's puttin' his cross to. The fool can be signin' his life away
without knowin' what he's at.

I love my mother, hard woman though she is. She goes
around dressed better than Queen Victoria even though I've
got holes in my pants. But it doesn't bother me. I know people

say she could have afforded to dress us kids better. But that doesn't matter. She's twice the woman Queen Victoria was and she's probably twice the man I am. She's supposed to be mean. Just because she won't let anybody put anythin' across her. It was my mother who took in Matty Cocklin and brought him up with us lot when his mother died in my mother's lodgin' house.

17

Bare Fists and Boxing Gloves

In 1905 my father was forty-five and was retired from the Ring. Though not from fightin', by any means. Because he was what he was, because he was big Harry Robinson, and because he was the brother of the great Johnny Robinson, people would always seek him out. That sort of thing always happens to a fightin' man. Especially when he's past his best. The young uns, in particular, always want to chance their arm. They always want to say they beat the man who beat the man who beat so and so. Just like with conkers. The hundred-and-eighty-sevenser hasn't necessarily bust 187 conkers. It only has to beat one conker – the hundred-and-eighty-sixer. When these fellers tell the tale they always forget to say that the man they beat was old, out of condition or drunk. Only that they beat him or that they gave him a good run.

I remember one ugly feller who had it in for my father like that. Every now and again he'd come round to the lodgin' house lookin' for Harry Robinson. We'd say he was out or busy. But this feller always wanted to try conclusions with my father. He wanted to beat Harry Robinson just once and then he'd be satisfied. He admitted it, every time. Whenever my father heard he was there he'd take him out into the yard and

they'd have a set-to. My father wouldn't even bother to take
his waistcoat off. Just his jacket. This feller was tough and
he was good. But he was neither tough enough nor good
enough for my father. After they'd finished they'd both wash
the blood off in the rain barrel and my father would tell him
to beat it, and not come back. But he'd be back. As sure as
night follows day. The last time he came my father had just
come back from the pub after the day's work. It was about 6
o'clock.

When he saw this feller my father says to him, 'What the
hell do you want? I'm tired and I want my tea. Why don't
you go into a corner and play with yourself?'

'Not so fast, Harry,' this feller says. 'Are you scared or somethin'?'

'Go and loss yourself, Jack. And take your mates with you.
Come back some Sunday mornin' and we'll go to Mass together. If you promise to go to Confession first that is.'

'That's fightin' talk, Harry. And I hear the bells ringin'.'

My father turned away and walked into the house. A
couple of minutes later there was a loud bangin' on the door.
Then a little while after that a brick came flyin' through the
window where my mother was standin' doin' the cookin'.

'You'd better go and fettle him, Harry, or I'll go and do
him myself,' says my mother. My father got up from the table
where he was lookin' at the sportin' paper. He slowly walked
to the door and pushed my mother aside.

'Keep it in the oven, Sally,' he says. 'This won't take me
long.' He shut the door behind him. We all looked out the
window.

'Watch this,' said my mother to all of us. 'Careful you
don't miss a move.'

'Right, Jack. How many of they are you? Five? You're
callin' the tune, Jack. How do you want it? One at a time,
or all together?'

'Just me, Harry. That's all you've got to deal with. I've
brought Bill here to act as referee. Tom as my second, Fred as
yours, and . . .'

'Get on with it and don't waste any more of my time,' says
my father as he takes off his waistcoat and hangs it on the

pump handle. This other feller then took his hat off and threw it on top of my father's waistcoat.

'Nobody caps my clothes. Next time bring a hat-rack.' My father kicked the hat off the pump handle and it landed in the rain barrel.

'Don't,' shouted Jack. 'He's too much for you!' But Tom rushed at my father like a bat out of hell. When he got there he got hit so hard in the belly that he vomited before he hit the ground.

'The next one gets drowned in that butt.'

'Here's spit in your eye, Harry Robinson!' And Jack cockled on the yard.

'This time it's the finish,' said my father. 'I've had enough of you.'

This Jack feller punched my father in the ear and then kicked his shin. The two of them went to the ground and wrestled. Both of them were swearin' like mad. My father butted him in the face and Jack hit him in the throat and my father crashed against the hen-cree and fell into the swill. He got up and they squared up to each other again. They both threw punches at the same time and their fists clashed with a crack like a hammer on a pig's skull. My father's left and the other feller's right.

'You've smashed my hand, you clumsy swine!'

'I'll smash more than that before I'm through with you,' said my father. And then he hit this feller so hard on the side of the head and followed up with such a smack in the middle of his face. The likes of which I've never seen. The feller went down and without waitin' for him to get to his feet, my father dragged him up and again he hit him just as before. The feller's face was like potted meat. All blood and pulp.

'Had enough?'

Jack opened his mouth and some awful stuff came weepin' out. One more punch like that and he was finished. You could see his jaw was completely smashed. My father turned to the other two fellers and said, 'Now, get out of my yard. And take that fool with you.'

One of the blokes was cryin' like a baby and another was bein' as sick as a dog. My father walked over to the rain barrel

F

and washed his face and hands. He put on his waistcoat and arranged his watch-chain just how he wanted it. Then he came in and said, 'Put my dinner out, Sally. I'm ready for it now.'

And all this only a few months after my father had been bad with rheumatic fever. He'd been drinkin' at the Long Bar one night and these fellers had been talkin' about the days when Uncle Johnny had used to swim the Tyne to escape the police. They were kiddin' my father on that he couldn't do it. Not now.

'I'll tell ye what I'll do,' says my father. 'If there's just one of yous lot man enough to do the same, I'll bet ye a fiver I can beat him.'

'What! On a night like this, Harry? Why it's pissin' down, man.'

'Tonight, and right now! As soon as I've finished my beer, I'll race any man here. There and back.'

'We were only pullin' your leg, man.'

'Aye, well I'm not,' says my father. 'Who is to be? If nobody stands up, none of you buggers will ever drink with me again.'

'Howay, man. Harry. It was just a bit of fun.'

There was always a big crowd around my father. He laughed out loud, and some stupid bugger says, 'There ye are, Harry, we've let ye off the hook. I knew ye wouldn't have really done it.'

My father grabbed this feller by the neck and says, 'You're the one, sonny boy. I don't know you. But I know what you are. Follow me down to the landin' and get in or I'll bash your brains out!'

'I've got no money to bet ye with, and . . .'

'Forget the money. Just get goin'.'

Somebody said, 'He's too drunk, Harry. He's only a kid.'

'Then high time he learned to watch his manners,' says my father, pushin' this young feller out the door. More than fifty of them went down to the river in the pitch dark. My father was so annoyed he didn't even take his clothes off. Just his jacket and boots.

'Can ye swim?' says my father.

'Aye, he can swim all right, Harry,' says somebody. 'I've seen him.'

'Right then,' says my father.

The young feller was peerin' over the side lookin' into the black water to see if there was anythin' in the way. My father gives him such a kick up the arse he went flyin' in. My father handed his watch and chain and wallet to somebody, dived straight in, and off he went. He lost sight of the other feller. Everybody was cheerin' in the dark. By the time my father got back there was twice as many people as there was before. The young feller was already bein' helped out.

'Did he make it?' says my father. 'There and back?'

'Yes, that he did, Harry. Fair and square.'

'That's good enough for me.'

'Look, I'm very sorry for what I said, Mr Robinson. I didn't mean it. I didn't really know . . .'

'Aye, well, you know now. Too bad you couldn't back yourself. Pass my wallet, Thomas. Here's half-a-dollar. Now beat it!'

The water had been freezin'. It was still rainin', and my father had been in the water a long time. The upshot of it was the fever two days later. He was bad with it for weeks and it took a lot out of him. After that my father never went out without a cap.

When I was fourteen I left school. Geordie left the year before. He was a far better scholar than me – in fact he was the best of the whole lot of us. But I was a better boxer than him. My father taught us to fight from the time we were old enough to make a fist. But although we always fought each other and the other kids with bare fists, when we went in the ring we had to use gloves. Professional fightin' was lawful in most places by 1891 – provided ye used gloves and abided by the National Sporting Club Rules. From that time, it was boxin'. And prize-fightin' – the Old Style – went out for good.

But kids weren't allowed to box in public. Ye had to be a certain age. About twenty-one. Or at least look as though ye were a man. This meant that when we left school my father couldn't match us against proper boxers so he sent us to learn a trade. I went to serve my time as a plater and riveter in the shipyards and Geordie went to work on the buildin's. He could have been a scholar, our Geordie, if he'd wanted. But like me, he couldn't wait for the day when he could step into a real boxin' ring. I liked fightin'. He loved it. So we went to our jobs and trained to fight at nights and at weekends. My father used to take us to see all the good fighters. We usually saw two a week. Mondays and Saturdays were always great boxin' nights. We were interested in all sports and we used to go and see all sorts of things. Runnin', scullin', football. Anythin' to do with trained athletes. Whatever my father thought would be good for us. We saw Jack Munro wrestle Franz Joseph of Austria for £100-a-side at the Newcastle Empire. Munro won in thirteen minutes. You're not allowed to wrestle or throw a man in boxin' nowadays but ye did in my father and Uncle Johnny's time. Next to boxin,' wrestlin's the best sport.

18

Francie

I was eighteen when I met Francie Nichol. That was in 1909. She was a year older than me. At one time she used to come round the doors sellin' her fish and stuff. My mother used to buy from her and so did the lodgers. I'd known Francie for a long time really. Her mob used to play with ours when we were kids. I'd liked her then even though she was a Protestant and I even made her my special. But when I was about fourteen we fell out. At least I packed her in when we heard about what one of her sisters had done. I hadn't seen her for years since. She had left the district and gone to live in North Shields or Jarrow or some place and I had started work in the shipyards. I was apprenticed to a plater and riveter. I knew she used to come round our way but I never bumped into her because she'd be long gone by the time I came back from work. But one day she'd apparently seen our Harry in town and he'd fetched her back to see my mother. They were havin' a saucer of tea together when I came in. I didn't speak to her or take any notice of her or anythin'. I just got about my own business, while watchin' her out the corner of my eye. There she was, pretendin' not to know that I was there. And I was doin' the same thing myself.

She'd not half changed. She was always a bonny lass. And tough with it. But she'd bloomed in the years since I last saw her. Hair all done up. Fancy lookin' skirts. Very big chest and plenty of colour in her. Quite a prize she looked, for any man. Anyway, as soon as she was sure I'd seen her, off she goes. Head up straight. All stuck up and proud she flounces out as though she owned the place. I finished washin' myself and went after her.

Well the top and bottom of it was that we got in with one another again, and in the October of 1909 we got wed. Not long afterwards, we moved to South Bank. My work was shifted to Middlesbrough, and Francie was expectin'. We'd only been there a few weeks when my father sent for me to come back to train for an important knockout competition that was bein' held in the January. Next thing is, Francie's back. She'd packed up everythin' and come back to Shields. She was full of hell, moanin' about the boxin' and about me not stickin' in at the shipyards. And all that sort of tripe. My father had a word with her and said he'd put her in charge of the Thrift Street lodgin' house. We could live there, I could carry on with my boxin', and she could earn herself some money lookin' after the lodgers. That should keep her happy. But no, she still wasn't satisfied. She then thinks that the lodgers are beneath her. Says she'd been brought up respectable and all that. She only had to stick at it and we'd probably get the Thrift Street lodgin' house for ourselves one day. My father had his own in Long Row. My mother had hers in Mill Street. And our Harry had one belongin' to himself in Barrington Street. It's a good regular income. I can fight and she can clean. Anyway,

I told her she'd just have to get on with it. And that was that.
So, like it or not, she buckled to.

On Christmas Day Alfie was born, but he was a weaklin'.
And he always was. And weaklin's are neither use nor orna-
ment. Anyway, come January, I entered for this knockout
competition. And on the 10th January, 1910, out of thirty-one
boxers, I was the winner. And I won it in the best way. By
knockin' out Jim Pattison in the decidin' bout. For the rest
of the year my father could only get me a few fights. I was
well known on Tyneside but not outside. My father wanted
me to fight the best men in England. But that takes time.
Men with big reputations don't want to chance them on
unknowns.

Stoker Allan comes from Durham. Ned's his real name but
everybody just calls him 'Stoker'. He was one-time champion
of the Navy, and a gamer boxer I've never met. Yet he's as
quiet as a mouse and he wouldn't harm a fly. Quick he is. If
you're walkin' down the lane with him and a couple of
pigeons fly out, he'll shout, 'Catcha pigeon, Johnny! Catcha
pigeon!' And away he'll go after them. There's feathers all
over the bloody place. But he lets them go again. He doesn't
hurt them. 'See, Johnny,' he'll say. 'Catcha pigeon, catcha
pigeon! It'll do ye good! Keeps ye on your toes, it does!' I've
seen some tattooed men in my time, but, by, he takes some
beatin'. He's like a pig in shit down at my father's in Long
Row. Comparin' his snakes and ladies with the sailors'. He
came to Tyneside to fight me but once he got in with our
Lily that put the kybosh on it. It's all right to spar or do
exhibitions in the family. But it's not done to have a contest.
Nobody does it. Same with our Geordie. Since Geordie took
up with Scotch Lizzie, she and our Lily go everywhere together. They sing together on the stage. Newcastle, Sunderland,
Hartlepool. Some say Lizzie's the best. Some say it's our Lily.
As far as I'm concerned they're both good. They've both won
singin' competitions on their own. So what does it matter.

Although I go to Stoker's fights and he always comes to
mine, we don't knock about together much. I like a drink.
He never touches it. Mostly I go round with Jack Lynch and
Joe Hancock. They are my main pals although I've got lots

of others. We can always make up a gang. Sometimes with the Callaghans. Since I left the shipyard and Matty married Liza Creamer, I don't see much of him now. The trouble with Matty is he's like our Geordie. Always lookin' for a fight. Anywhere. The docks, the street, the pubs. He's a damned good scrapper, mind, but it's always done out of a Ring. Francie doesn't like him at all and I must admit he is very vulgar with women. Our Geordie's rough but at least he's not like that. Trouble with Geordie is he's such an argumentative feller. Specially with me. He'll argue about nowt just for the sake of it. And he'll tie ye up with words. He can talk like a lawyer when he has a mind. Stretches things a bit, but he can tell a good tale. Anybody in Shields'd tell ye that.

After a year or so in the Thrift Street lodgin' house, Francie was gettin' on like a house on fire. She'd made herself friendly to the lodgers and they seemed to be likin' her in return. They respected her as well. Because when she first went in, I taught her how to defend herself. And where to hit where it hurts. This was so that when I was away she could look after herself by herself. She still hadn't taken to the boxin' mind. And she didn't like me goin' away trainin'. She didn't like me havin' the special meals me father makes for me, either. And she hates the idea of me takin' our Lily and not her. Now Lily is my sister. She loves the fightin' game and knows all about it. She understands what's needed. She knows how to talk to the men. Francie doesn't. Lily can mix with men. Francie can't. Lily's a beautiful woman. And she can take a drink. That's more that I can say for Francie. It's good for a man when he's out makin' matches, to have a smart and clever woman by his side. And at least with our Lily I can trust her. What I mean is that seein' as she's my sister – well, ye know what I mean by that.

Francie's forever with bairns. She's got plenty to keep her occupied without meddlin' in my affairs. Her place is at home and her duty is to her husband. That's me. She'll do just as she's told and put up with it. Her job is to have my dinner ready when I come home for it. And to have it fit to eat no matter what time it is. She seems to think I should be sittin' bouncin' babies on my lap all day. What she doesn't realise is that a boy belongs to a mother until he becomes a lad. Then the father takes over. A girl belongs to a mother until she's old enough to get married. Mother and sister are above wives and daughters to any man. And that's the way it should be. A mother or a sister are straighter with ye than a wife or a daughter ever is. And cunnin' liars are of no use to man or beast. A man's word is his promise. Francie can't see that. But then, she was fetched up amongst a bedlam of babblin' women. She wasn't brought up to know what really counts. She doesn't know what it is to have a man to respect.

Francie doesn't like my mother. And my mother doesn't care too much for her, either. But I think it's Francie's fault. She's far too bloody proud. If my mother or my father offer her anythin' – no matter how small – she just won't take it. Many's the time my father said to her, 'There's my jacket hangin' up behind the door, Francie. If ye want owt, just help yourself.' But will she? Will she hell. 'I wouldn't dream of doin' a thing like that, Mr Robinson,' she'll say. 'It'd be like stealin'.' My father just laughs. But it really annoys my mother. Even though Francie's scared of my mother – she's twice her size and much tougher, she will keep on standin' up to her. In her stupid, proud way. My mother's never taken her hand to her but she will one day. And if she does Francie'll be bloody sorry. She's forever askin' for it. My mother was once sortin' her out and sayin' some pretty bad things to her when she jumps up and says, 'I was brought up just as well as you, Mrs Robinson. At least I never went round the streets sellin' chalk and rubbin' stone.' How the hell my mother didn't lay her out there and then, I'll never know. But she's certainly never forgot it. Mind, Francie isn't daft. Before she said her piece to my mother, she opened the front door and the back door, ready to make a run for it.

But my father's got a real soft spot for Francie. And she loves him as well. Whenever she's bakin' she'll always send a pie down to my father at the Model. He always stays there and eats on his own. He sometimes takes her out in his pony and trap. My mother doesn't care much for that. My father'll even take Francie's word against mine. Once I went away to Durham with some of the boys for a bit of a spree. Francie

came down after me and I sent her packin'. Next thing I
know, my father sends for me. When I got back, he was waitin'
for me with his cane. The one he uses to tan his lodgers with –
he won't use his fists on ye unless ye ask for it. Anyway, I got
flayed with his cane till even Francie couldn't stand no more.

I even take her out, myself, sometimes. I don't know what
else I can do for her. I give her all my wages, and all my
winnin's. She keeps it all, but whenever I ask for a tenner to
go to London or to the races, there's always a fuss. And she
always has to have the last word. No wonder I clout her now
and again.

I once asked her for some money for to go to the Dogs.
She says, no. I told her she could take the same and spend it
on herself. But she says she needed all the money for the
house. So I took the bank-book and chucked it on the fire.
And what did she say? She says, 'You stupid bugger, ye. Go
and look in the mirror and see how daft ye look.' What can
ye do with a woman like that? Except give her a good hidin'?

I wear a dut and a stiff collar, and sometimes a straw benger,
just to suit her. I hardly ever wear my cap and muffler nowadays.

Mind, for all that I'm very fond of her. If only she knew
her place and kept to it, she'd be all right. And I wouldn't ask
for more.

19

The Real Ring

It was great to win the Thompson Knockout Competition for
nine-stone novices. I was absolutely thrilled with that. I thought
I could never be happier. But that was nowt compared with
my first real professional fight. It was against Joe Blyth on
the 7th March, 1911. At nine stone. Fifteen rounds for £15-

a-side and a purse. With St James' Hall, Newcastle, as the
venue. I cannot forget a single thing about it. The excitement!
Oh, man, I could hardly believe it. The build-up. The fight!
And then afterwards. I don't know what was the best. I
enjoyed it all. Every minute of it. I felt like one of the gladiators
of old. And I was treated like one as well. Of course my father
didn't say very much. He said it was nowt. Just the start. Not
to rest on my laurels. And things like that. But I could see
he was pleased. And I know he was proud. He couldn't help
himself from showin' it. But my mother made no bones about
the way she felt. She might have a hard face but it wasn't that
night. She couldn't stop herself from laughin', she was so glad.
There's nothin' more she wants than for me to be a champion.
Of England. The world. Anywhere.

I wasn't a bit nervous before the fight. I was in tip-top
condition. I had trained very hard for it. The ropes. Runnin'.
Eatin'. No drinkin'. I never smoked at all then. Hours and
hours on the punch-ball. All kinds of exercises to harden my
muscles. Shadow boxin' and sparrin' from mornin' till night.
And no woman. I couldn't have been better. I only had to
loss one pound. And that took nothin' out of me. I had plenty
cold showers. But no Turkish baths. I didn't have to. I must
have looked pretty good judgin' by all the remarks I was
gettin'. Long before I ever got into the Ring. My father had
been paradin' me round all the fightin' pubs for weeks to make
sure I would get good support. And I did. My father knew
everybody in the fight game. And everybody knew him. I don't
think there was a feller in Shields who hadn't heard of Big
Harry Robinson.

'We'll be expectin' to see you there,' he'd say to one. And
'I'll be lookin' out for you at the fight,' he'd say to another.
They knew they all had to be there. And they would have
been as well. In any case. But my father wanted to make sure.
A lot of them would kid him on and say, 'Is he as good as
you yet, Harry?'

'Heh, heh,' my father would say. 'When he's that good he
won't need me to show him 'round. But he's better than you
are, I can tell ye that, for sure. He'd scatter the whole bloody
lot of ye, if I set him loose.'

I would never say owt like that. Uncle Johnny must have been even worse. It embarrasses me. All this fightin' talk. I realise that ye had to do it in my father's day when they didn't have promoters like they do now. Everything ye said had to come out like a challenge. That was the way ye got known. However, I just smile when my father talks like that. He knows what he's doin'. So I just keep my mouth shut. Anyway, before my first big fight my father did plenty talkin'. Plenty for him, that is. He'd have a drink everywhere we went. The most I got was a half shandy. He would shove his way to the front of the crowd. I'd be standin' back a bit. 'Howay, lad!' he'd shout. 'Come over here and let them have a look at ye.' Mind, I felt very proud to get all this attention. First time I'd had it. He was used to it and he knew just exactly how to handle a crowd. He'd let nobody buy me a drink. We'd stay for mebbes half an hour and then go off to another place. He'd bust the door wide open and go in with his big hands by his sides or sometimes in his pockets. Jacket open at the front. Heavy gold chain stretched across his huge chest. Cigar in his mouth. Not the slightest sign of emotion. He never gets himself worked up about anythin'. I'd have on my green jumper and shorts and I would put my arm up to wave or shake hands. He would keep his hands where they were and just nod. I'm proud of my father. Everybody feels safe when he's there. No matter how rough or tough the company.

By the time came for the fight, I was ready and rarin' to go. At the weigh-in the promoters and stakeholders were all there. With the referee. And the important well-wishers who had been allowed in. I shook hands with Joe Blyth and stepped on the scales at 8 st. 11½ lb. Joe tipped nine stone exactly. He didn't look any better than me. He seemed a canny enough feller as well. We weren't allowed to talk much to each other except to say 'Good Luck'. By night-time, ferry-loads and train-loads of South Shields lads were pourin' into Newcastle. My father and our Geordie were with me in the dressin' room. And my trainer Charley of course. He was the only one who was excited. He couldn't keep still.

'Get a grip of yourself, Charley,' said my father. 'Ye'll make the lad edgy.'

Geordie was keep goin' out to look in the hall. 'There's thousands here tonight, Johnny,' he says. 'All come to see ye make mincemeat of that feller out there.'

'Don't underestimate him, Geordie. But see ye give him a good thrashin', all the same, Johnny.'

'Righto, dad,' I says. 'I promise I'll do my best.'

'Aye. Ye'd better.'

When they came to call me, my father walked out first. Takin' his time. 'Keep right beside me, son. Don't stop. And don't pay any attention to anybody. Just keep your head up and look straight ahead.' When we stepped into the aisle everybody was cheerin' like mad and shoutin' all sorts of things to me. All good. Nothin' bad. The ring was quite high up and very brightly lit. I followed my father towards it. As we got near I saw my mother and our Lily right in the front. My mother must have been the biggest woman in the hall. She had all her jewellery on and it was sparklin' away as she waved about. Lily looked beautiful with her great big hat and all her feathers. Next to her, Lizzie. Just the same. Then our Harry with his bowler hat and stern face. I've never seen so many high-shiners in one place. Oh, and that good, strong smell of pipe baccy, cigar smoke and manly sweat.

The Master of Ceremonies was announcin' the contest. But I wasn't listenin'. I was thinkin' about all my father had taught me. Not just about how to fight. I could do that without thinkin'. But why. The greatest sport in the world. There I was, goin' to defend myself with just my own two hands. I was goin' to face a man who was goin' to try and knock me down in front of hundreds of people. Not only was I goin' to stop him, I was goin' to knock him down instead. Once in there, I was on my own. Nobody could help me. Some would be shoutin' for me to beat the livin' daylights out of him. And others would be shoutin' for him to beat the livin' daylights out of me. No wonder it's called the Noble Art. There's nothin' finer. I was dancin' first on one foot. And then on the other. I was tinglin' from my head to my feet. I started throwin' punches in the air and the crowd started roarin' like mad. I clenched my fists inside my gloves and the new shiney leather squeaked and squeaked. I thought of one of those big, hard bunches smashin' into his face and puttin' him straight down. So he wouldn't be able to get up again. I blew hard down my nose. The other feller heard and looked at me. It seemed to scare him. I did it again. My boots were brand new. Beautiful, tight, neat laces. Fastened by Charley so they would never come undone, no matter how hard I jumped. Then the bell went and we were at it.

I got the first blow in. It was a straight left. My best punch. Blyth is known for bein' an aggressive fighter and he pressed me hard. But I had the advantage in height and reach and was able to keep him off me most of the time. He never caught me in the face. His tactics were to go for the body like I expected he would do. His first couple stung my belly a bit. But after a while I hardly felt them. And every time he hit me it made me all the more determined. For every one from him in the body I gave him two in the face. At first ye don't really like the idea of hittin' a feller who's never done anythin' to ye, who you've maybe never even seen before. But as soon as he hits you, things are different. Then after one clinch his head cracked my teeth. I felt the salty taste of my own blood in my mouth. And that did it. I would make him pay for that. The fight went the full distance but I knew I had won even before the ref held my hand up. Geordie jumped into the ring and held my other hand up. My father winked. My mother was shoutin' like a man. Our Lily came up into the ring and was huggin' and kissin' me. My father pulled her away and told her to get back to her seat. Everybody was standin' up in the hall, and cheerin' away. I don't think I had a single enemy that night. I forgot all about Joe Blyth as I waved and waved. I couldn't stop smilin'.

Geordie says, 'You're grinnin' like a silly cat, ye daft bugger.'

'I know. But I cannot help meself,' I said. 'I'm so pleased.'

Charley made me put my muffler on and he carefully damped my towel over my head. As we walked up the gangway followin' my father, I don't know how many hands shook mine. It must have been hundreds. People kept pushin' their way into the dressin' room while I was gettin' a shower. I felt in great condition. I could have done another fifteen rounds there and then. Easily. When we got dressed and came outside of St James', there was a huge crowd waitin' for me. We sang all the way back to Shields on the train.

What a night that was. It wasn't till I'd got back to bed in Thrift Street that my body began to smart and throb. But it didn't matter at all. It was the first time I'd been with Francie for nearly a month.

20

Featherweight Champion of the North

Not long before my fight with Joe Blyth of North Shields, little Johnny was born. Let's see, the contest was in March so he'd be born in February some time. Healthy little feller as well. 1911 was a good year for me. Not only was I gettin' a lot of good fights, I was gettin' my picture put in the paper. Every time. Boxin' pose, of course. My father was really proud. First I beat Joe Blyth, then I lost to Mickey Kelly of New-castle. Funny feller, Mickey. He was like an old man. He'd been retired from the Ring for years. He used to be a prize-fighter and then decided to come back when the gloves came in because he thought that anybody who used gloves would be easy meat. He was right as well. He gave a lot of other good fellers a hidin', besides me. Next I beat Battlin' Phillips of Hartlepool in June, then Barney Cain in July. Jim Lewis of Wales also in July, George Ruddick of Manchester in September, and then Charley Harte of Leeds again in Sep-tember. Then I drew with Jim Lewis in October. That was a good month because I also beat Jack Williams of Sheffield and Joe Fox of Leeds – and Joe Fox is a good man. Not only was I havin' contests all the year through, I was also givin' exhibitions with our Geordie and Stoker in between times. I was comin' on well now. I had my own followin' wherever I went. I was recognised every time I stepped out into the street. I was hailed as the Northern Featherweight Champion. And my father was very pleased with me. Quite satisfied anyway.

1912 wasn't quite such a good year. I didn't get so many good fights. My father was careful about how he matched me now. He wouldn't have me take on anybody unless they were straight out of the top drawer. And many of those weren't so keen now that I was at the top. Not that I was at my prime then – I'm still not, even yet.

I started off the year by drawin' with Jerry Delaney of Bradford. The referee made it a draw. But there was nearly a riot on because everybody seemed to think I should have won. But I don't begrudge sharin' the honours with a man like Jerry. He's a good boxer and a good man. In April I beat Munro Grainger of Wales, and in October I drew with Alex Lambert of London at St James's Hall. In December I lost to Wally Pickard of Newmarket.

In the January of 1913, just before my return match with Alex Lambert, little Joe was born. And a few days after the fight, little Alfie died. Just like with fightin', ye win one ye lose one. And draws don't count. My father doesn't allow me to stay with Francie when I'm trainin' for a fight. I know for my own good that I haven't to go with her, but he won't even let me see her. Just to be on the safe side, I suppose. That's why he usually packs me off to Morpeth with Charley Whyte. Charley is my trainer. My father got him for me when I gave up the shipyard and started boxin' full time. My father has a room specially done out for me at the Mill Street lodgin' house. Sometimes I go down to Comical Corner to spar with the other lads. That's where I met Walter Callaghan and his brother Tommy. And Peter Kane. All good lads. In fact, my father likes Walter so much he often has him up to the lodgin' house as a sparrin' partner for me. He likes Walter because he never pulls his punches. And because he's clever with his hands and his feet. Some sparrin' partners are scared to hit ye in case ye get mad at them and floor them. But not Wally. He couldn't care less. The promoters like Will Curley and Tom Murphy are tryin' to get him matched with Jimmy Wilde of Wales. They hope to attract Jimmy to St James's Hall,

Newcastle. They say he's a good lad as well. Tough and quick. Should be a good scrap, that, if it comes off.

Anyway, back to my record. . . . The January fight I had with Lambert ended in another draw. Then in June I drew with Joe Starmer of Kettering. Two lousey draws off the stot. That really got my father goin'. He didn't like that at all. He says a draw is only one punch off a defeat. In July I beat George Groves of Canning Town and things were lookin' up again.

Last year, 1913, was a funny kind of year in some ways. All sorts of odd things happened. First the Government said we were goin' to have a war with Germany. Then they said we weren't. Off and on like that it's been all year. Some folks still think there's goin' to be one. But nobody seems bothered. I'm not. Jimmy Burrows died after a match in London. The newspapers said it was a legitimate stomach blow that did it. These things happen from time to time. Ye can even get killed playin' cricket if ye get hit hard enough in the right place. Pat Breslin apparently stood up in a ring in Scotland and challenged a crowd of miners who were booin' him after a bad decision. In the finish he fired a revolver at them. They say he would have been lynched if the police hadn't got there in time. Young Fox beat Joe Mooney in New York. He's goin' places all right. There's some trouble brewin' in the North of Ireland by the looks of things. The rugby clubs have cancelled all their matches to let the stadiums be used for drillin' soldiers. Sam Langford caused quite a surprise by beatin' Joe Jeanette in Paris. The French say he's the new World Heavyweight. The Americans say it's still Jack Johnson. But after the pathetic show he put on against Jim Johnson I think he's had it now. He's been lettin' himself go to the dogs for the last couple of years. The French seem to be stagin' a lot of the big fights these days. The newspapers say it's because French women like big black men. They also say a lot of pretty bad things, besides. Ye can never tell what women are goin' to do next. In this country they're settin' fire to churches and all sorts of things. Starvin' themselves to death in prison. This Pankhurst woman wants a good kick up the backside. The French are producin' some good men of their own. Their Carpentier feller certainly didn't mess about with our Bombardier. Either time.

I was twenty-three years old, and though I say it myself, I was in magnificent condition. Just the way a boxer should be. Pink and glowin' with health. All over. If ye pressed my skin so it went white, straightaway it became pink again without leavin' any dints. My skin was smooth but not shiny. And without a single spot or mottle. Hair black. No grease, no dandruff. Eyes bright. I could shift my gaze quickly. I could see without lookin', feel without touchin', and hear without listenin'. My ears were alive, not flat. No wax in my ears, no snot in my nose. My pee was neither sweet nor sour and would have been fit to drink. My motions were brown and firm with a good smell. My spit, clear, and neither thick or frothy. Everythin' came out easy. Good-sized half-moons in all my nails, no cracks. When I went to bed I went straight to sleep without ever a nightmare. And when I woke up I got straight up. I couldn't stay in bed once I'd had my proper sleep. I could control any muscle – arm, leg, back, stomach – any one, anywhere. I sprang from a chair and walked as though the ground was made of sponge. All my reactions were like lightnin', and without thinkin'. Aches I never had. Pains neither. Throbs, yes. Smarts, yes. But only after a fight. Fear, no. Keenness, yes. Worry, no. Excitement, yes. Hate, no. Disgust, yes. Love, no. Respect, yes. That's not to say I'm not very fond of some people. But love's soft. I'm not rough but I think I'm pretty tough. I try my best to be like my dad.

Schfutt! Schfutt! Schfutt-schfutt!!

'That's my style. Left! left! Left-right!!

When a man is like that, the women all want him. People think ye don't want a woman just because ye don't take them. The truth is, that's when ye want one most. But what they don't realise is that sweat ye needs get rid of, but your spunk ye must keep to yourself. It's more use to you than it is to a woman. What takes weeks to build up is lost in a couple of minutes. A demandin' woman is like a leech drainin' a man's goodness and sappin' his strength. It costs a woman nowt. It might cost a man a victory. When he's strong, they're after him. When he's weak, they've no time for him – and he's no use to heself either.

No matter what anybody else might think, the Robinsons are hard but we are not cruel. We all love fightin' but there are none of us bullies. We aren't like soldiers who blow people to pieces that they don't even know. We only fight those who want to fight us. Prize-fighters and boxers aren't led into a ring like a bull on a rope. They're in there for one reason. And one reason only. Because they love to fight. People talk about hungry fighters. That is a load of utter tripe. A man might squabble with another over a crust of bread, but no man steps into a fightin' ring after months of trainin' just because he's got no grub in his belly. Nobody will make us fight. And nobody will stop us, either. We hit only to hurt, not to maim. Ye soon get to know that if ye hit a man in one place the blood'll come out red, and that if ye hit him in another, it'll come out orange. But every fighter I've ever known or heard of would rather break a man's body than injure his dignity. In our family, although we have always fought among ourselves, we aren't contestin'. We are only toughenin' each other up a bit. A fightin' man is more use to his kids than a milksop.

Every time I've had a fight, I always come straight back to Thrift Street first, to Francie. I leave my father and my friends to do the celebratin'. My father takes all my cups and medals to Mill Street, and I come back to Thrift Street for my supper and then I go to bed. I can't be bothered to talk to Francie about the fight. If she asks how I got on, I just tell her to read the papers next mornin'. Mind, the next day, I always treat the lodgers if I win. They can either have a pint of beer or a free night's board. My father does the same at his lodgin' house. That's who I got the idea off.

It's good to get back to my own little home. After months of trainin' and talkin' about nowt but boxin', boxin', boxin', I like a bit of peace and quiet. Francie's a good cook and always has a nice supper ready for me. And the place is always so neat and clean. She hasn't got much, but what she has got, she does well with. The table's always so tidy.

At my mother's, in Mill Street, the big table has everythin' in the world on it from the parrot to a scrubbin' brush. All mixed up with food, buckets of beer, clothes, papers, boots, dishes, hats, knives, pipes and baccy. Over there, everythin's cooked in a pan or a basin and just stuck on the table. Straight out of the oven. If ye want owt, ye just dig in and help yourself. No sittin' down to a proper dinner with knives and forks or owt like that. My mother'll sit with her clay pipe in her mouth, a jug of beer in one hand, and half a loaf of bread in the other. There's always all kinds of rough characters in the place and it's always in a mess. Talkin', singin' and fightin'. All goin' on under my mother's eye. Mind, it's a different story when my father's there. She has this great big tallboy dresser. On it are all the fightin' prizes and nowt else. My father won't have them touched. All over the panels are chalk marks. Where my mother does her accounts. There's a false-drawer in the top where she keeps her money. She doesn't trust banks and has it hidden all over the place. My father's dog, Sweep, stays there. People say it's a great-dane crossed with a black horse. It certainly looks like it. He got it off one of the sailors. It's got a collar on which says, 'I'm Harry Robinson's dog. Who's dog are you?' My father's also got this coloured parrot which he hangs out the window. It shouts, 'Ten to one, bar one! What ye bettin' the day, Harry me boy!' My father now has lodgin' houses in Mill Street, Long Row, Barrington Street, Thrift Street, St Hilda's Lane, Spring Lane, Ferry Street and Winchester Street. All of them are only ten minutes walk away, and all are near to the Market. That's where all the pubs are. Eight to choose from. My father drinks in Jackson's Long Bar in Union Alley with his pals, I drink in the Black and Grey with mine, and Geordie in the Adam and Eve. Our Harry drinks at home. Only hard liquor. His wife ran away with a doctor in London and he's killin' himself with drink in Shields.

Ye have to be very strong-willed not to drink where we live.

21

Man's Stuff

Things were goin' fairly smoothly for me until November came. I'd smelt my own blood before. But I'd never had to wallow in it. I'd lost before. But I'd never been humiliated.

At 9 o'clock on the 17th November, 1913 I was matched to box the best of twenty rounds with Harry Sterling of London. It was at St James' Hall, Newcastle. This was to be one of the most important fights I've ever had and my father and the promoters had worked hard to get me this chance. Sterling was the holder of two championship belts and there was tremendous interest in the outcome. All over the country. We had to fight at 9 st. 4 lb., and I had a hell of a job to make that weight. My father wants to keep me in the featherweight class because of the experience. There's probably more good featherweights about than anybody. A lot of people say I should let my weight go, and that I could fight more naturally around the eleven-stone mark. My father says I have to bide my time. But every contest I have now it gets harder and harder to keep my weight down. I have to eat less. Train harder. And sweat more often. And that means Turkish baths. The trouble with them is that they sap you too much. Your strength comes out with the sweat. I'm much bigger than Harry Sterling and I was paid out before I ever went into the ring. Not that I dare tell that to my father.

Anyway, what happened was that I got a real hidin' off Sterling. That was the first time the referee had ever stopped a fight on my account. I was up and down like a yo-yo. I don't know how many times I hit the boards. But every time I did my father would be shoutin' and cursin' at me. Callin' me spineless and stupid. Everybody in the hall must have heard him. And when I went to my corner between rounds – it went on till the twelfth – I thought he was goin' to thrash me himself. I know I deserved it. Well, when the referee finally called a halt and I put my towel on to leave the ring, some of my pals were pattin' me on the back and sayin', 'Hard luck, Johnny.' ... 'Better luck next time, Johnny.' ... 'Ye put on a good show, Johnny.' ... 'At least ye didn't give in, Johnny.' And things like that. Mind ye, there was plenty booin' me as well. My father came up and shoved me off to the dressin' room. He was tellin' my sympathisers to go to hell, and that I wasn't worth supportin' and things like that. I felt really ashamed of myself. On the train back to Shields he wouldn't even sit beside me. He just said that when we got there I had to go straight to Mill Street because he wanted to see me. I knew I was goin' to get what for and I'd rather have it then than later. When we got back to his house he says, 'Well, can ye stand? Or do ye want to lie on the floor?'

My mother says to him, 'Let him sit down, Harry. The lad must be tired.'

'Tired! He's been restin' all bloody night!'

'It's all right, mother. I'll stand,' I says.

'Too bloody sure ye'll stand, ye sod, ye. I've seen some pretty sorry exhibitions in my time. But never one like that. You've let me down. Your mother! Your brothers! Your sisters! Your pals! Your supporters! Your family! Everybody! And yourself! I gave ye the best fightin' name in England. And you've gone and disgraced it. Champion featherweight of the North? Champion featherbrain more like it!'

'I'm not complainin', Dad,' I says. 'I was beaten fair and square.'

'I bloody well am! I'm complainin' all right! You weren't beaten fair and square, ye bloody sap. He sucked ye in and farted ye out. A man half your size!'

'Johnny's a different sort of fighter, though, Harry. Not like ...'

'He's no bloody fighter at all. That's what's the matter with him. He's got no heart. He didn't even try.'

'Yes, Harry, but don't ye think ye should let him fight at

his natural weight? This weight-makin's takin' a hell of a lot out of his hide.'

'Don't make excuses for him, woman. I know what I'm talkin' about. Go and fetch my jug of beer. And you get back to your bloody gin and mind your own bloody business. I'll handle him.

'Ye might be a cleverer boxer than Geordie but by hell ye couldn't hold a candle to him when it comes to fightin'. You lack the most important ingredient of all. Ye cannot punish. And ye can't take it, either. And don't give me any more of your blab about it bein' wrong to smash another man's face in. If he's in there, he's askin' for it. Whether he wants it or not. Same as you are. You're in there to hit and be hit. Pity has no place in a fightin' ring. Remember that! Any man can be a hero or a coward as the mood takes him. A man's no man at all unless he has power over himself. Over his feelin's. And any feelin' in a Ring is a sign of weakness. It'll do ye down as much as two blind eyes would. Well, what have ye got to say for yourself? Come on speak your mind while you've got the chance.'

'All that I can say is that I'm sorry, Dad. I'll try and do better next time.'

'Tryin' is not enough. You've got to win. That's what you're there for. The trouble is that the whole game has become as soft as shit. Gloves! Dancin'! Dodgin'! It all makes me sick. When Figg and Broughton started it all off they were handy with the sword as well. And that is what fightin' is all about. Not dookin' out of the way. But parry and thrust. Block and hit. Tradin' one blow for a harder one. Nobody used to ask for quarter, or get it. A fighter has no regard for blood or pain. That's for women. It should be the way it used to be. No limits on rounds. No limits on blows. No draws. And none of these ridiculous referees with their points for little taps that wouldn't hurt a bloody fly. One time, a man was only beat when he couldn't come to scratch. No messin' about. None of your fannyin' around. That pansy, Queensberry, spoilt it all with his damned gloves and bandages. Then those silly buggers down in London with their soppy Sporting Club Rules finished the game off. What with Queensberry's ten-second counts and his three-minute rounds. And his bannin' huggin' and wrestlin'. That pampered twat should have stuck to his winin' and dinin' and whorin'. And left the Noble Art to men. Real men. Not bloody sissies like himself. Huggin' was grapplin' with your man so ye could clash him to the ground and wind him. If ye go anywhere near a man these days the bloody referee steps in. Stop! Box on. Stop! Box on. Ye don't know where the hell ye are. Let the poor buggers get on with it. And fight. That's what they are there for. A man doesn't clinch a man to give him a bloody kiss. But to get his measure. Only fifteen rounds exceptin' for championship fights. And then only twenty. Ye don't even get the chance to get started. It takes at least fifteen to get warmed up. What you've got to wear and not to wear. Hell's bloody bells!

'Why do ye think I put ye in the ring in the first place, eh? To give ye a chance to make your mark in life. To make a man of ye! That's why! And that's only bloody why! The way to make money out of boxin' is to bet. Not to box. I've given you and Francie a lodgin' house to keep ye. But I never intended ye to treat boxin' like a hobby. The way you're treatin' it.

'Go on, Johnny. Get out. It makes me sick just to look at ye. And see you're back here at 8 o'clock sharp in the mornin'. You're goin' straight into trainin' for Johnny Condon.

'Come back here, Johnny. Gis a look at that eye ... You s-t-u-p-i-d bugger!

'Sally! Fetch the jar of leeches.

'The only reason your brains aren't hangin' out of your ears into the bargain is because ye haven't got any. Right, lie there and keep your mouth shut.'

My father's always been known for bein' a man of few words. He spoke more that night than I've ever heard him speak. I knew he was right of course. As I was walkin' home I was thinkin' about the difference between him and me and Geordie and me. Geordie and my father love fightin'. So does Stoker. And Wally Callaghan. But I can't help thinkin' sometimes that it's just a sport like anythin' else. Of course these thoughts I keep to myself. Geordie loves a brawl in the street or in a pub as much as in the Ring. He'd fight in Church if

he had to. He's a good brother to me though and I
always like to have him in my corner. And I like doin' the
same for him. Sometimes we do exhibitions together. But mostly
when we fight together it's to settle an argument. Geordie
always wants to beat me. I hate fightin' outside. But Geordie
doesn't care a jot. A couple of months ago we were down on
Marsden beach with a few of our pals. We'd all had a beer
and some of the lads started on about who was really the
best. Geordie or me. Geordie said it was him. And his gang
egged him on to have a go at me. There was no stoppin'
him. So we got stuck into each other. In no time there was
a crowd round us, yellin' and cheerin'. Everybody loves a free
fight. There was no seconds, no ring, no rounds. Just plenty
punchin'. Before we'd been at it ten minutes the police come
chargin' up. Now our Geordie has always had a great line
in patter. Before I'd got a chance to open my mouth he told
them I'd pinched his clothes, and then I'd attacked him.
He got clean away and I got marched off to jail. When
Geordie got home he told my father what had happened and
asked him to bail me out. Geordie said he had no money
himself, and that he couldn't go anyway because of what he'd
told the police. My father said 'Ah't! Let the stupid bugger
stop there. Maybe it'll teach him a lesson.'

When I got home to Thrift Street, Francie was still up.

'Sorry about the fight, Johnny. Stoker and Lily have just
been in to tell is all about it.'

'Go to bed!'

'Has your father been on to ye? Did he give ye a good
tellin' off?'

'Mind your own business, Francie. Go and make my supper.'

'Have ye had nowt at your mother's, then?'

'We were too busy talkin'.'

'Too busy listenin', ye mean. I bet you didn't do much
talkin'. Why don't ye give it up, man Johnny?'

So I took a hold of her and sloshed her one. That shut her
up.

22
No Choice

It's now 1st January, 1914. New Year's Day.

I sorted out Johnny Condon last week and I'm back in tip-top form. Next, I challenged Jerry Delaney at his fight the other night. He's a good 'un. And then I've got Harry Sterling comin' up shortly. The deposits are already laid. This time it'll be different. I'm havin' a good run just now. Mind, I feel a bit queer today. Never been like this before . . .

Our little Johnny and Joe are comin' on well now. Johnny's nearly three and Joe goin' on for two. They'll manage all right. Johnny's got over his burnt arm, and little Joe never ails nowt. If one of them doesn't turn out to be a fighter, I'll be damned. Both of them healthy and fine lookin'. Johnny's a bit on the small side but with colour enough. And Joe looks like he was born in sawdust. My father will be proud of them. So would Uncle Johnny. Francie keeps talkin' about wantin' them to grow up to be somethin' else. But what else is there? What else could they do? They'll have to be fighters. One may be better than the other, and they may be different weights. . . . But both of them fighters!! That's what they'll want to be anyway. No other life for them. I wonder what I'd have been if I hadn't been born a boxer? Some people say I should have been a priest. Who ever heard of a boxin' priest? Anyway I'm not. And that's that. Francie's a canny lass really but if I gave her her own way she'd have me a bloody riveter. A riveter? Who in hell goes to Heaven because he's a riveter? Any fool can be a riveter. Anyway I'm not any good at rivetin'. I'm a boxer? I'm only twenty-four, but I'm a boxer and people respect me because of that. Crowds wouldn't follow me all over the place to see me knock a rivet into a hole. But when I get into a ring to knock a good man into the floor. . . . Well that's different. Everybody'll come to see me. . . .

Francie might be tough enough in her own way but she's too soft for me. Always yappin' on about the boxin'. Always on to me to give it up. If it was her or the boxin', it would be her I'd give up. Her father's only a brickie, and that's no better than rivetin'. If he carried as many hods as he does bottles he'd be a better man than he is now. He's one of those fellers that only knows how to knock a woman about. A good hidin' would do him the world of good. . . .

I don't really know whether I'd want to be a boxer or not if I had the choice. I certainly don't care much for rivetin'. But my father said I had to get a job until such time as I could show him whether I was a fighter or not. Now he thinks that I am, that's it. I love my father and I respect him. He knows best. He says I was cut out for boxin' and that if I get to the top I could be rich and famous. . . .

I don't know what the hell's the matter with me today. Daft things seem to be happenin'. I can't see straight, yet the whole of my life has passed before my eyes as though it had all happened only this mornin'. My Grandfather Rafferty, Uncle Johnny – everythin'. It's a very strange feelin'. I'm not a broodin' man but I just seem as though I cannot help myself thinkin' about all sorts of things. I've got aches in my muscles and pains in my bones. I'm roastin' one minute, and freezin' cold and shiverin' the next. I'm soaked with sweat like I've never been even in a Turkish bath. I've got pains in my head and bells ringin' in my ears. I must be goin' crazy or somethin'. My hands and feet are all tinglin' and I feel as though I want to be sick but I can't. Even my heart's beatin' funny. I'm so weak I cannot even move the bedclothes and they're like a ton weight. I must have the flu or somethin'. I've never had it before. But this is what it must be like. I never realized that flu could be as bad as this. When I move my eyes I can see all kinds of funny lights. I'm not half dizzy. I'll have to get better soon. I've got to beat Sterling this time. But

I just can't seem to snap out of it. People seem to be here but they seem to be far away along a tunnel. I can see my dad's face down a well all the time . . .

Epilogue

My name is Joe Robinson, and the young man lying ill in the Thrift Street Lodging House, in January, 1914, recalling his story, was my grandfather. Shortly after his senses left him, he tried to throttle both his father and his wife – my grandmother. In between bouts of great violence when he tore bedding to shreds and smashed furniture, he appeared composed – even getting up to comb his hair. At times he seemed to speak rationally. Most of the time he raved: cursing one and all one minute, and declaring his love and loyalty the next. Sometimes he just lay singing the old sentimental songs for hours on end. The doctors apparently could do nothing for him. They said that he was in the last stages of double pneumonia and that he was beyond all earthly aid. All the while, his father never left his bedside.

On 4th January, 1914 Johnny Robinson died. He was twenty-four years old, and left behind a wife, also twenty-four, and two boys whose ages added together came to less than three years. Johnny was buried from his father's lodging house in Mill Street. And many men cried in South Shields that day.

The Sporting Man, 8th January, 1914
The Funeral of the late Johnny Robinson, the Featherweight Champion of the North, took place yesterday afternoon from his residence in Mill Street, South Shields, in the presence of an enormous crowd. The large number of mourners included many well-known local sportsmen. The hearse was drawn by a team of four black horses and there was an open carriage containing many beautiful floral tributes including a wreath from St James' Hall, Newcastle.

The chief mourners were Mr and Mrs Henry Robinson (father and mother), Messrs George and Henry Robinson (brothers), Miss Mary Ellen Robinson and Mrs Allan (sisters), Stoker Allan (brother-in-law), Henry Robinson (nephew), Mrs Scott, Miss Nancy Constello (cousins) and Paddy Cairns (West Hartlepool). Others present included Messrs Richard Baker, Will Curly and Tom Murphy from St James' Hall; Tom Payne (world champion walker), Athol Nichol, who assisted Robinson in his training at Morpeth for his principal fight at the National Sporting Club; Tom Callaghan, Young Walters (Jarrow), Sam Johnson, Tom Ridley, Spider Carr, Billy Vardy, Henry Snaith (quoit champion), Steve Lloyd, Jimmy Lloyd, Mickey Kelly (Newcastle), Harry McDermott (an ex-champion featherweight boxer), Willy Wood (a former champion cyclist), Charles Slone, Patsy Logan, Luke Swales, Victor Layton and James Duncan.

The interment took place at Harton Cemetery, the Rev Father Bennet officiating.

Eight days later Harry Robinson was laid to rest beside his son in Harton Cemetery. Harry Robinson's death certificate also gave pneumonia as the cause of death, but all those who knew said Harry Robinson died of a broken heart.

✠ IN AFFECTIONATE REMEMBRANCE OF ✠

JOHNNY ROBINSON,

THE DEARLY BELOVED HUSBAND OF FRANCES ROBINSON,

Who departed this life January 4th, 1914,

AGED 24 YEARS.

———

INTERRED IN HARTON CEMETERY.

Johnny Robinson has crossed death's stream at last,
His life career in this world is past, ·
And now we would give him what is due,
For he was always game and true.

Straightforward and honourable to friend or foe,
Johnny was never known to to strike a coward's blow,
Fair play and justice was his plan,
As a boxer Johnny was every inch a man.

He met some of the best men of his day,
And bore many a splendid prize away,
He won the championship cup with pluck and skill,
Thousands remember his gallant battles still.

The North of England Feather-Weight Champion is now no
His early death many will deplore,   [more,
Johnny Robinson won a wondrous name,
As a sportsman will be handed down to fame.

One by one we all must surely go,
When death summons comes we never know,
So let us do our best for all mankind,
And leave a good example here behind.—G.R.

7—50